SIR HUGH MYDDELTON

SIR HUGH MYDDELTON

From the portrait by Cornelius Johnson in the Baltimore Museum of Art, Mary
Frick Jacobs Collection

SIR HUGH MYDDELTON

Entrepreneur and
Engineer

BY

J. W. GOUGH
Fellow of Oriel College, Oxford

OXFORD
AT THE CLARENDON PRESS
1964

Oxford University Press, Amen House, London E.C.4

GLASGOW NEW YORK TORONTO MELBOURNE WELLINGTON
BOMBAY CALCUTTA MADRAS KARACHI LAHORE DACCA
CAPE TOWN SALISBURY NAIROBI IBADAN ACCRA
KUALA LUMPUR HONG KONG

PREFACE

THIS is not a biography of Sir Hugh Myddelton; for that we should need much more than can now be discovered about his private life. Most of this book is concerned with his public career, and it seemed best to deal with each of his principal achievements separately. In order not to interrupt my account of these I have gathered together in the opening chapter what is known about the rest of his life, including his work as a goldsmith, and in the concluding chapter I describe briefly what subsequently became of his descendants.

It was Sir Arthur Russell, Bt., of Swallowfield Park, near Reading, who first suggested my writing about Myddelton, and I am sorry he did not live to see this book in print. I owe much to his encouragement and the advice he gave me about the mines in Cardiganshire. I am also grateful to Emeritus Professor A. H. Dodd, of Bangor, for his kind help over a number of questions about members of the Myddelton family. My chief debt is to Mr. G. C. Berry, M.A., a member of the statistical officer's staff at the Metropolitan Water Board, who has generously allowed me to draw on his own extensive knowledge of Myddelton's career. Apart from his published work, which I have used freely (on this see the Note on Sources, p. xi), Mr. Berry has constantly helped me by giving me references to printed and manuscript material, and answering my questions, and his comments have saved me from numerous mistakes. I should also like to thank Mr. David Piper, Keeper of the National Portrait Gallery, for his help in clearing up some problems about Sir Hugh Myddelton's portraits; Mr. Roger Ellis, Secretary of the Historical Manuscripts Commission; Miss Susan M. Hare, Librarian of the Goldsmiths' Company; and Mr. G. Milwyn Griffiths, Assistant Keeper in the Department of Manuscripts and Records in the National Library of Wales, Aberystwyth.

J. W. G.

Oriel College, Oxford, 14 May 1964

CONTENTS

LIST OF PLATES

NOTE ON SOURCES

I GIVE references in the footnotes to the sources on which this work is based. The place of publication of printed works, unless otherwise stated, is London. Besides these, the following may be mentioned:

CHAPTERS I AND VIII. For particulars about members of the Myddelton family and their pedigrees: W. Duncombe Pink, *Notes on the Middleton Family* (Chester, 1891; reprinted from *The Cheshire Sheaf*); G. Milner-Gibson-Cullum in *Miscellanea Genealogica et Heraldica*, 3rd series, vol. ii, parts 7 and 8 (1897); W. M. Myddelton, *Pedigree of the Family of Myddelton* . . . (Horncastle, 1910). See also Professor A. H. Dodd's article on the Myddelton family in *D.W.B.* There is also much information about various members of the family in the footnotes to the volume of *Chirk Castle Accounts, 1605–1666,* edited by W. M. Myddelton (privately printed, St. Albans, 1908).

CHAPTERS II–V. For accounts (of varying accuracy) of the New River and the London water-supply: W. Matthews, *Hydraulia; an Historical and Descriptive Account of the Water Works of London* . . . (1835); F. Clifford, *History of Private Bill Legislation*, ii (1887), c. viii; R. Sisley, *The London Water Supply, a Retrospect and a Survey* (1899); W. R. Scott, *The Constitution and Finance of . . . Joint Stock Companies* . . . (Cambridge, 1911), iii. 3–31. There is a brief account, based mainly on the city archives, in vol. ii of *London and the Kingdom* (1894), by R. R. Sharpe, who was records clerk in the Town Clerk's office. By far the best informed account of the making of the New River is in the lecture given by Mr. G. C. Berry on 25 January 1956 to the Honourable Society of Cymmrodorion, entitled 'Sir Hugh Myddelton and the New River', and published in the Society's *Transactions* for 1956 (1957), pp. 17–46. He has made extensive use not only of the city archives but also of the New River account books mentioned below (p. 36). These account books were formerly at the Land Revenue Office and are now at the Public Record Office. There are nine of them, L.R. 2/27–33, nos. 27 and 28 each consisting of two books. L.R. 2/34 contains a statement of moneys received from the king, copies of indentures, and other miscellaneous accounts connected with the New River. L.R. 2/35 ff. give details, street by street, of rents and fines paid by tenants from Lady Day 1614. These account books were indexed by M. S. Giuseppi in his *Guide to the Public Records* (1923), i. 171, where he states that the Land Revenue records were taken over by the Public Record Office in 1903, but the New River accounts seem to have been ignored by historians until comparatively recently, when Mr. Berry unearthed them. In 1948 Sir Jonathan Davidson included some quotations from the account books, based on Mr. Berry's researches, in his presidential address to the Institution of Civil Engineers. This is printed in the *Journal of the Institution of Civil Engineers*, vol. 31, pp. 1–13.

LIST OF ABBREVIATIONS

B.M.	British Museum
C.J.	*Commons Journals*
D.N.B.	*Dictionary of National Biography*
D.W.B.	*Dictionary of Welsh Biography*
G.B.	Great Britain
H.M.C.	Historical Manuscripts Commission
I.W.	Isle of Wight
L.J.	*Lords Journals*
M.W.B.	Metropolitan Water Board
N.L.W.	National Library of Wales
N.&Q.	*Notes and Queries*
P.C.	Privy Council
P.R.O.	Public Record Office
S.P.D.	*State Papers Domestic*
T.L.R.	Times Law Reports
V.C.H.	Victoria County History

I

CITIZEN AND GOLDSMITH OF LONDON

In spite of their English surname the Myddeltons, or Middletons, of Denbighshire were an old Welsh family, who claimed descent from Rhirid Flaidd, one of the nobility of medieval North Wales.[1] They called themselves Middleton when one of them in the fourteenth century married the daughter of Sir Alexander Middleton, of Middleton near Chirbury, in Shropshire. In the sixteenth century the main line of the Denbigh Middletons was established at Gwaenynog, a couple of miles west of the town; Richard Middleton, who belonged to a younger branch, was the first member sent to Parliament by the borough of Denbigh, in 1542, and Governor of Denbigh Castle at the beginning of Elizabeth's reign. He married Jane Dryhurst, daughter of an alderman of Denbigh, and had his home at Galch Hill, now a small farm about half-way between the town and Gwaenynog. He died in 1575, and his memorial brass in St. Marcella's (otherwise called Eglwys Wen or Whitchurch), the mother church of Denbigh, shows him and his wife flanked by their nine sons and seven daughters, all kneeling. The two best known of these, Thomas and Hugh, are commemorated by a tablet on the wall of their birthplace at Galch Hill.

Different branches of the family used a variety of forms of their surname. Richard of Galch Hill apparently signed his name 'Myddylton'; his sons Thomas and Hugh used the spelling 'Myddelton', and adhered to it with remarkable consistency, though Thomas sometimes spelt his name 'Middelton', and quite often referred to members of other branches of his family, and even his own brothers (including Hugh) as 'Middleton'. Other people, and official documents, more often than not referred to them as 'Middleton', but their descendants, and the Gwaenynog line, all

[1] See Note on Sources, p. xi.

firmly retained the form 'Myddelton', and nowadays this is the accepted spelling of the name for these branches of the family. Spelling was still erratic in Elizabethan times, but it is worth noticing that the village of Middleton, from which the family took its surname, and which was spelt 'Mildetune' in Domesday Book, as early as 1327 appears in the Subsidy Rolls as 'Myddeltone'. Myddeltons still live in Denbigh, and the name (spelt 'Myddleton') may be seen over shops in the town.[1]

A remarkably high proportion of Richard Myddelton's off-spring not only survived to manhood but also achieved eminence in their various ways. Some stayed at home, or not far from it. One of these was the eldest, Richard, who became the founder of another branch of the family at Wrexham; but of his eleven children three became London merchants, and two at least prospered sufficiently to be included among the original Adventurers in their uncle Hugh's New River. His brother Charles, the fifth son, and Foulk, or Fulke, the eighth, were both at some time closely associated in business in London with their brothers, but later returned to Wales; Charles to succeed his father as Governor of Denbigh Castle, Foulk to become High Sheriff of Denbighshire, and his brother Thomas's agent for the recovery of his 'Welsh debts'.[2] The third son, William, sought his fortune further afield, for after fighting in the Netherlands under Sir John Norris he settled there as a trader, married a Roman Catholic wife from Ghent, and became a Catholic himself.[3]

But in the Tudor age London was above all the place to which young men who wanted to make careers for themselves flocked, or were sent, from all over the country, and notably younger sons of the gentry. Many came from Wales, and among them were three, if not four,[4] of Richard Myddelton's younger sons. Thomas,

---

[1] The same spelling has crept into the tablet at Galch Hill. For different spellings of the Shropshire village of Middleton see E. Ekwall, *Concise Oxford Dictionary of English Place-Names.*

[2] Cf. A. H. Dodd, 'Mr. Myddelton the Merchant of Tower Street' in *Elizabethan Government and Society* (ed. S. T. Bindoff, J. Hurstfield, and C. H. Williams, 1961), p. 263.

[3] Prof. Dodd points out that writers on the Myddelton family have confused this William Myddelton with a namesake and cousin who became a sea-captain and bard, and composed a Welsh metrical version of the Psalms (op. cit., p. 250 n.). The latter's name, incidentally, is always spelt either 'Middleton' or 'Midleton'.

[4] The ninth and youngest son, Peter, is described as 'of St. Dunstan's in the East,

the fourth son (1550–1631), is an outstanding example of the wealth and success that could be won by an enterprising man. After serving his apprenticeship to a London grocer he became a freeman of the Grocers' Company in 1582. As such his principal trade was in sugar with the Low Countries, but besides this he also engaged in a great variety of commercial and financial transactions. He was a partner in many of the buccaneering ventures of Elizabethan times, and had shares in the Virginia Company and the East India Company, as well as (later) in his brother's New River. He became an alderman and sheriff of London, was knighted, and in 1613 he was Lord Mayor. He had been M.P. for Merioneth in 1597 and represented the City of London in the Parliaments of 1624–6. He also set up as a landowner, not only in Wales (in 1595 he bought the lordship of Chirk Castle, which has remained the property of his descendants ever since) but also in Essex, where he established himself in a country seat at Stansted Mountfitchet.[1]

Almost equally successful, though less is known about him, was the seventh son, Robert, described as merchant and skinner, or glover. His affairs prospered sufficiently for him, like his brother, to become one of the original Adventurers in the Virginia Company and the East India Company, as well as in the company that sought to open up the North West Passage. About 1588 he was established at Weymouth, where in 1593 he was associated with his brother Thomas and others in 'victualling of divers barkes', apparently engaged in reprisals against Spanish shipping. Later he took over part of Thomas's business interests and for a time acted as one of his resident agents in trading depots at Middelburg and Caen.[2] Like his brothers he entered Parliament, and was one of the members for Weymouth and Melcombe Regis in 1604–11, and for London in 1614.

Merchant', but not much is known of his activities. In the 1590's Thomas's ledger shows him acting, together with Robert, as Thomas's agent or associate at a depot for the cloth trade with France at Caen. He died in 1595.

[1] See Prof. Dodd's study of his career in *Elizabethan Government and Society*. This is based largely on his ledger, one of the Chirk Castle documents now deposited in the N.L.W. (Chirk F. 12540). See also the article on it by D. Evan Jones in *N.L.W. Journal*, vol. i, no. 2 (1939).

[2] A. H. Dodd, op. cit., pp. 252, 255, 257, and 260.

Hugh Myddelton was the sixth of his father's nine sons, but the exact date of his birth is uncertain. In his *Lives of the Engineers* Samuel Smiles thought it was about 1555,[1] but it has usually been said that he was born in or about 1560.[2] The parish registers of Henllan, in which Galch Hill is situated, do not begin till later, and the date may have been arrived at simply by reckoning back from 1631, the date of his death, when he is said to have been 71. The only authority for this, however, as cited in the *Dictionary of National Biography*, is the Probate Act Book of the Canterbury Prerogative Court; but investigation shows that while this gives the date on which his will was proved, it does not in fact mention his age.[3] Still, there is nothing inherently improbable in the year 1560 as the date of his birth, and it is confirmed by the inscription *Aetatis suae 68, Anno Domini 1628*, painted on what appears to be the original of his portrait by Cornelius Johnson.[4]

In 1576 Hugh followed his elder brother up to London, and on 2 April he was apprenticed to Thomas Hartop (also spelt Hartopp or Hartoppe) of the Goldsmiths' Company.[5] The exact date when he received his freedom is uncertain, for the volume of Court Minutes covering the years 1579–92 is missing, but Hartop's will, dated 13 September 1582, indicates that he was then still an apprentice. In 1585 he spent the months of April, May, and June at Antwerp, where his brother evidently still felt some responsibility for looking after him, for he paid £3. 5s. 6d. for 'his table [board] in the English howse' there, besides £3. 1s. 4d. 'for a barrel chest that he bought'. It was apparently while Hugh was in the Netherlands that his freedom of the Goldsmiths' Company was granted, and soon after his return to London he married. Thomas's

[1] Mainly because his mother died in 1565 (as the memorial at Whitchurch shows) and he had three younger brothers. Cf. the footnote (omitted in later editions) in *Lives of the Engineers* (1861), i. 98. Hugh also had at least one younger sister.

[2] On 9 Feb. 1960 the *Daily Telegraph* published an article stating that he was born '400 years ago this month', but substantiation of this statement has not been forthcoming.

[3] I owe this to Mr. G. C. Berry of the Metropolitan Water Board.

[4] At any rate he himself believed he was 68 in 1628. On different versions of this portrait see Appendix, p. 145.

[5] For information about his career as a goldsmith I am indebted to the Librarian of the Goldsmiths' Company. If he had been born in 1555 he would have been close on 21 when he began his apprenticeship, which though not impossible seems unlikely.

financial assistance was called upon on both occasions. He paid
£7. 18s. for his brother's freedom and spent £2. 15s. for the
purchase in London of 'his wyffes gowne cloth against his
wedding'.[1] Hugh was twice married, but not much is known
about his first wife except that her name was Anne and that she
was the daughter of Richard Collins of Lichfield. She was a widow
when he married her, her first husband having been a man named
Richard Edwards, described as 'of London', but (judging by his
name) a Welshman by origin. He may possibly have been related
to the Rev. John Edwards, of Llansannan (the seat of another
branch of the Myddelton family), who became the second husband
of Hugh's eldest brother Richard's wife. She died childless, at the
age of 54, on 11 January 1597, and was buried in St. Matthew's,
Friday Street, the church where her husband worshipped for
many years, and in which he was ultimately to be buried himself.

Hugh Myddelton's name first appears as a liveryman of the
Goldsmiths' Company in 1592; in 1594 he in turn took on as
an apprentice Richard, son of William Hartopp, who presumably
was some relation of his old master. In 1604, and again in 1605,
he became a Warden of the company; in 1610 he was Prime
Warden, and he held this office for a second time in 1624. As a
goldsmith he learned and practised the craft of making and testing
articles of gold and silver; but goldsmiths also dealt extensively
in the precious metals, coined money as well as plate, and carried
out many of the money-changing and money-lending functions
nowadays performed by bankers. Nor were a goldsmith's trading
activities confined to gold and silver. His company was one of
the richest and most powerful of the great city companies,[2] and,
as the late Professor Tawney pointed out, the rule called 'the
custom of London' allowed a member of any of the twelve great
companies to practise not only his own company's particular
craft or trade but also any other he pleased, and 'by the early

[1] Thomas Myddelton's ledger, all under date 5 Nov. 1585. Thomas's payments were
apparently advances rather than gifts, for an entry a few lines lower down records Hugh's
repayment of £7.

[2] See T. F. Reddaway, 'The London Goldsmiths circa 1500', in Trans. R. Hist. Soc.,
5th ser., vol. 12 (1962), pp. 49–62, for an account of the company a little before Myddelton's time. The Goldsmiths ranked 'fifth in the order of precedence', after the Mercers,
Grocers, Drapers, and Fishmongers, but ahead of the rest of the twelve great companies.

seventeenth century a single company might include among its members practitioners of a dozen or more different trades'.[1] Tawney refers to 'the variety of irons kept in the fire by some of Cranfield's associates, who, without abandoning the trade which is their speciality, move in a continuous whirl of temporary and shifting partnerships to exploit a commercial *coup* or grant by the Crown'.[2]

We get much the same impression of multifarious activity from the entries in Thomas Myddelton's ledger, and once Hugh had gained the freedom of his company his brother was able to assist him in more than one money-making venture. A good example is the so-called 'Goldsmiths' Voyage' of 1589, apparently a buccaneering expedition against Spain, in which three of the Myddelton brothers, Thomas, Hugh, and Foulk participated, together with other business associates. Thomas financed their shares in this by means of £700 of customs money, then lying in his hands because Sir Francis Walsingham, the lessee of certain customs, had deputed their collection to him.[3] In ventures of this kind losses as well as gains were common, but the ethics of the time saw nothing wrong in using public funds for private speculation, and not all their ventures were as risky as this. For example, Hugh also obtained straightforward business orders through his brother, one of the earliest being in 1585, when Thomas and his partners wanted three gilt bowls made for presentation to one of their customers in the Netherlands, Gerard de Malynes.[4] In January 1594 Hugh Myddelton supplied Sir John Fortescue with a jewel costing £120, called a 'carcanet of pearle', for presentation to Queen Elizabeth;[5] soon after James I's accession he executed an order for the King himself. His Queen, as is well known, was inordinately fond of jewellery, which the King lavished upon her; one of his presents, a diamond pendant costing £250, was supplied by Hugh Myddelton.[6]

[1] R. H. Tawney, *Business and Politics under James I* (Cambridge, 1958), p. 9 n.
[2] Ibid, pp. 79, 80.   [3] A. H. Dodd, op. cit., p. 254.
[4] Ibid., p. 253.
[5] According to W. M. Myddelton, *Pedigree of the Family of Myddelton* (Horncastle, 1910), p. 18.
[6] *Cal. S.P.D. 1603–10*, p. 187 (9 Jan. 1605); F. Devon, *Issues of the Exchequer . . . during the Reign of James I* (1836), p. 19.

Numerous entries in Thomas's ledger show the brothers constantly helping one another out with temporary loans of cash in varying amounts, or combining to lend money to third parties, sometimes in quite small sums, sometimes as much as £100 or £300 at a time, generally repaid in instalments. On occasion Thomas lent money within the family 'of goodwill freely', as he put it on 5 October 1588, when Hugh repaid £40 he had borrowed for some months on account of their brother Foulk, described as Hugh's 'servant'; on another occasion (18 May 1590) Thomas and Hugh combined to provide £250 worth of 'marriage goods' for their sister Barbara. More often, however, Thomas's advances were on a commercial basis, for after starting in trade he had gone on to make a regular business of money-lending. Much of what he advanced was secured on mortgages of land, but he also became what Professor Dodd has called 'a pawnbroker in the grand manner'.[1] He 'accepted almost anything negotiable', but his favourite securities were gold or jewels, possibly because Hugh could help him to appraise and if necessary dispose of them. We get a glimpse of one of Hugh's dealings in the money-lending business in a letter to Sir Robert Cecil, dated 5 December 1601, from Arthur Hall. As students of Elizabethan parliamentary history will remember, Hall had been in trouble before. On this occasion, it seems, he had been six months in the Fleet prison on account of some debts, in one of which Myddelton was concerned. The details are obscure, but Hall now appealed to Cecil to come to his rescue.[2]

A close business associate of both Thomas and Hugh Myddelton was another Welshman, Robert Bateman, a member of a family from Haverfordwest, into which their brother Charles had married. Bateman belonged to the Skinners' Company, and was a prominent city merchant. He was Thomas Myddelton's partner and agent in numerous business deals,[3] and later became one of Hugh's partners both in the New River scheme and also in the reclamation of Brading Harbour. In the foundation-charter of the New River Company he is named as its first

[1] A. H. Dodd, op. cit., p. 262.

[2] H.M.C. *Cecil MSS.* xi, 512; H. G. Wright, *The Life and Works of Arthur Hall of Grantham* (Manchester, 1919), p. 107.

[3] A. H. Dodd, op. cit., p. 269.

Deputy-Governor, with Hugh Myddelton as Governor. Robert Myddelton's daughter Jane married another member of the Bateman family, William, who was also an Adventurer in the New River.

Another example of the close interconnexions of the London merchant aristocracy of those days can be seen in the membership of a jury appointed on 9 May 1611, when James I went to the Star Chamber to 'see his moneys of gold and silver to be taken out of the pixe and to be tryed'. The coinage was tested by the 'trial of the pyx' every year, but it was most unusual for a king or queen to witness the process in person. On this occasion, when James himself 'gave a Jurie of sixteene of the most honest, skilfullest and best reputed Gold-smiths their oathes and charge for tryall of the moneyes', the list of names is headed by 'Hugh Middleton' and those of three other Wardens.[1] Two other names, William Beareblocke and Gayus Newman, are of interest, for James Beareblocke and Gabriel Newman (son of Gaius, who died in 1613, and was buried in St. Matthew's, Friday Street) were among the original members of the New River Company.

For Hugh Myddelton, as for Thomas, and indeed for Welshmen generally, the claims of kinship were always strong, and only less strong was a predilection for their fellow-countrymen. On the other hand, while to say they married for money would be pointless, for it was an age of arranged marriages, their marriages were undoubtedly advantageous, helping to extend the range of their business contacts, and the interconnexions between their wives is certainly suggestive. Thomas's first wife (he married four times altogether) was the daughter of a skinner named Richard Saltonstall; his brother Robert Myddelton married her widowed sister, whose previous husband seems to have been a relative of one of Thomas's partners. His second wife was the widow of John Olmstead, or Olmestede, of Ingatestone in Essex, and the stepdaughter of a London alderman and business associate. In 1598 Elizabeth Olmstead, her daughter by her first marriage, became Hugh's second wife.[2] Thomas promised her £100 worth

---

[1] E. Howes, *Continuation of John Stow's Annales or a Generall Chronicle of England* (1631), p. 1000.

[2] He thus married his brother's stepdaughter. If he was born in 1560, his first wife must have been eighteen years older than he, and his second twenty years younger.

of 'marriage goods', but the way he paid (in May of the follow-ing year) was by writing that amount off a debt Hugh owed him at the time. Elizabeth Olmstead, who was her father's heiress, brought her husband a valuable accession of property, and his marriage to a wife of rank and fortune is in itself an indication of the position he had then attained.

The influence he could wield may also be inferred from the benefits he had secured not long before for his native town. Though his business career was centred in London he never lost his interest in Denbigh, and he was instrumental in obtaining a new charter for the borough. He paid a special visit for the occasion, and on 20 September 1597 put his signature to the first set of by-laws in the borough register. This volume also contains, besides a list of officers and members of the corporation in which his name appears as the first of the 'Aldermen and Capitall Bur-gesses', some sentences in Welsh in Myddelton's handwriting, beginning *Tafod aur yngenau dedwydd* [a golden tongue is in the mouth of the blessed], with other aphorisms, and expressions of regret at having to part from his brethren at Denbigh. Visits to North Wales, however, may not always have been so enjoyable as this, and an episode a few years later reminds us of the law-lessness that was apt to break out in Tudor times, at any rate in remoter parts of the country, where a great landlord might still sometimes defy the law. On 30 March 1600 the Privy Council wrote to the 'Highe Sheryfe of the countye of Denbighe' on the subject of 'very greivous complaints exhibited unto us concerning divers great misdemeanors, outrages and vyolences' committed by 'servauntes and followers' of Sir John Salusbury,[1] 'in rescuing of prisoners and commytting affrayes'. They went on to refer to 'one disorder amongst the rest', which 'seemeth to be very insolent and outragious, in that some of them assaulted Foulke Middleton, an Alderman and Justice of the Peace in the towne and burroughe of Denbighe, going to assyst the inferior officers for her Majesty's service, who is sore hurte'. This was Hugh's younger brother, and the letter goes on to say that 'one Hugh Middleton, that defended the Alderman,' was 'so wounded as

---

[1] One of the leading magnates in the county.

there is no hope of his life'.[1] If this was our Hugh Myddelton the report that reached the Privy Council must have greatly exaggerated the seriousness of his injuries; but perhaps it was only a cousin, for Myddeltons were numerous about Denbigh, and Hugh was a fairly common name in Wales. At any rate, if he was the victim of this attack he recovered, and it must have been about this time, as he recalled in a letter some twenty-five years later, that he made what he called his 'first undertaking of public works'—an attempt to find coal in the neighbourhood of Denbigh.[2] This proved a failure, but he kept up his connexion with the borough, and shortly afterwards became its Recorder. He also represented it in all the Parliaments from 1603 to 1628, and remained a 'capital burgess' until his death.

On 5 September 1616 the corporation minuted as follows:

Be it remembered (for the glorye of God, and the perpetuall memoriall of the giver) to our posteritie, that Hughe Myddelton, Esquire, Cittizen and Gouldsmith of London, and first Capitall Burges, and first Alderman named in the late Charter, granted by the late Queen Elizabeth (of famous memorye), hath freelye bestowed upon the nowe Aldermen, Bayliffes, and Capitall Burgesses of this Towne, and *ther* successors for ever, *on*[e] great silver Cupp, of thirtie ounces gouldsmythes weight, with his name upon it, and his arms, with motto: 'Omnia ex Deo'.

It was ordered that the cup was

not to be used by any officer alone, or any other privat man, but to be only used at the publick meetings of the said Aldermen, Bayliffes, and Capitall Burgesses, and *ther* successors for ever, or at any publique meetings for the credit of this Towne; and to be kept in no one man's custody, but in the same chest *wher* the said Charter is kept.

Myddelton presented similar cups to the corporations of Ruthin, of which he also became a burgess, and where he had acquired property, and Oswestry,[3] and a silver-gilt one to the head of his family, William Myddelton, at Gwaenynog. It has generally, and

---

[1] *Acts P.C. 1599–1600*, p. 216.   [2] See below, pp. 98, 101.

[3] *Archaeologia Cambrensis*, 2nd ser., no. 1 (1850), pp. 134–6; J. Williams, *Ancient and Modern Denbigh* (Denbigh, 1856), pp. 156–7. The cups are still in the possession of these boroughs.

very naturally, been assumed that these cups were made from the silver produced at his own mines in Cardiganshire, but this can hardly have been so, for he did not take a lease of the mines until 17 February in the following year (1617). The cup presented to the Gwaenynog Myddeltons was put up for sale in 1922 and bought by the Goldsmiths' Company, in whose possession it now is. The hallmark on it shows that it was made in 1599, and the likelihood is that not only this cup but the other cups as well were made in Myddelton's workshop, in the ordinary way of business, from purchased materials.[1]

Like his brother Thomas, Hugh Myddelton invested some of his capital in land in the neighbourhood of Denbigh and Ruthin, and though the documentary evidence is scanty it is clear that he regarded charity and generosity as part of a rich man's duty. On 10 April 1609 he wrote to Sir John Salusbury about the loan of some money. The letter contains such characteristic and interesting touches, and so few of his letters have survived, that this,[2] and another letter written about a year later, deserve reproduction in full:

Upon the receate of your letter I delivered this berer Robert Glynne to your use 300 li. and the deade which I hadd for 105 li. payable the 24th Maie next which makithe uppe 400 li. I received of hym the deade and bonde sealed by you & others which (in my opinion) are verie reasonable, but have seide I meant plainlie (as I assure myself you doe) and what is donn, is owt of Love, and not of a greedie desire of anie advantadge. I did not abate for the use of the 200 li. the 3 li. 10s. dewe, for the tyme past, nore the xx s. which I paid the screvener for the writinge because you writt nothinge thereof. I praye you paie

---

[1] According to J. B. Carrington and G. R. Hughes, *The Plate of the Worshipful Company of Goldsmiths* (Oxford, 1926), pp. 57–59, the Gwaenynog cup was presented to Hugh Myddelton by the Goldsmiths' Company to celebrate the completion of the New River in 1613, but I know of no evidence that any such presentation was made, and it is surely very unlikely that he would have given away a cup presented on such an occasion.

[2] N.L.W. Bachymbyd Letters, no. 8. I have expanded contractions, but retained the original spelling. The letter is summarized in *Cal. Salusbury Correspondence* (Cardiff, 1954), p. 306. Besides Sir John Salusbury, Myddelton also had business dealings with another local magnate in North Wales, Sir John Wynn of Gwydir, in the Conway valley. On 30 Nov. 1604 he paid Sir John £40, but whether this was an advance or the repayment of a loan is not clear (*Cal. Wynn Papers*, N.L.W., letter 315). There are other references to Wynn's dealings with Myddelton in letters 273 and 778.

it this berer whom I have apointed to deliver the same, to be dystri-
buted against this good tyme. This berer hath related unto mee the
Cause whie you sent noe sooner for the 300 li. for which I ame
hartelie sorie, but right glad of your amendement which I pray God
long cotyneue. Protestinge that the 300 li. hath bynn ever since the
14th Februarie last redy in chest for you, dailie expectinge to heare
from you. I have undertaken a matter, which I praye God prosper,
that will cost mee all my poore meanese, this berer will enforme you
thereof, I cannot be Idell. This well fynyshed, the next shalbe in Walles
(God willinge) unto whose most holly protection with my hartiest
Comendacons I committ you from London this 10th of Aprill 1609.

I pray you Comende me to
Cousin Wm. Salesbury

Your ever assured Loving Cousin
to Comaund

Hughe Myddelton.

'This good time' was no doubt the approaching Easter; the costly
undertaking on which he had just embarked was, of course, the
New River. Does his promise that 'the next shall be in Wales'
mean that he was already planning to work the mines, to which
he turned soon after the New River had been made?

In the middle of the next year opposition to the New River was
at its height and must have given him plenty of cause for anxiety,
yet he found time to concern himself with the purchase of some
property for charitable purposes near Denbigh. There was some
delay in completing the business, and he wrote to some 'Lovinge
Cousins and Frinds' as follows:[1]

I receved your letter of the 16th of Aprill percevinge therby that
the assurance touching those Landes bought of Mr. John Price to
the use of the poore are come into your handes but that possession is
not delivered you by reason of my cousin Salesbury being in Sherop-
shire hopinge (because you write that wilbe don within a sennight) the
same is perfected longe since whereas I desire to be satysfied and to receive the counterpaine towtching the particuler I ame satysfied, and
gladd that my proceeding therein Likith you soe well I have alsoe paid
upon the receate of the Acquittance by Cousin Davy Holland of
Hendree the 60 li. unto hym to the use of the poore of Whitford, accordinge to the Codicell anexed to my Cousin's Will, not Douptinge of

1 N.L.W. MS. Downing 109.

your Conscionable care in the well dystributing or bestowing thereof accordinge to his trew menynge and soe with my verie hartie cousinlie Loves and like thanks for your pains and kindnesse in this charitable busenesse, Comitt you to God from London this 25th July 1610

Your assured Lovinge
Cousin and Frind
Hugh Myddelton.

We get a few glimpses of Myddelton as a landlord in some letters addressed to him by his tenants at Ruthin, and the impression they give is that while he was careful in the management of his estates, at the same time he enjoyed his tenants' goodwill. One letter, to 'my approved good Landelorde Hughe Middelton Esquier at the gilded Tonne in Cheapside London', is endorsed 'from Robt ap Hugh the Tennant'. After acknowledging receipt of a letter from Myddelton, the writer admits 'that yor nephew John Middelton hath often warned and willed as well myself and all other your tenants . . . to plant quicksettes in our tenementes . . . and I myselfe have all readie now of late sett some quicke settes and other plantes in that tenement which I hould'. He goes on to profess his readiness 'to doo you anie other service to the uttermost of my power without compulsion'.[1]

Incidentally these letters throw light on the situation of Myddelton's London house, where no doubt, as was then customary, he also had his workshop as a goldsmith. Samuel Smiles and other biographers have implied that throughout his working life he carried on business in 'Bassishaw' (now Basinghall) Street, but it can only have been in his later years that he lived there.[2] At first he set up shop in Cheapside;[3] then, in the early 1600's, letters from Ruthin were addressed to his house in Wood Street,[4] and

---

[1] N.L.W. Ruthin Castle Letters, no. 921. Robert ap Hugh may conceivably have been related to 'Rees Uphughes', who carried Pond's level while the New River was being made in 1612 (see below, p. 51).

[2] He was there by Jan. 1627, when he wrote from that address to recommend a young man to Secretary Conway (*Cal. S.P.D., 1627–8*, p. 20).

[3] Besides the Ruthin letter just quoted he is represented as working in Cheapside in a funeral elegy to his father Richard Myddelton, which must have been composed (or touched up) at least eight years after its subject's death in 1575. (Information in a letter to me from Prof. A. H. Dodd.)

[4] N.L.W. Ruthin Castle Letters, nos. 924, 925 (5 Mar. 1604).

he was still there ten years later, when he had New River water laid on.[1] He apparently wanted to move before this, for in 1612 he offered £240 for a lease of the Goldsmiths' Company's 'garden-house and garden, with the bowling alley and grass plat', but this offer does not appear to have been accepted.[2] It must have been about this time, however, while the New River was under construction, that he acquired a country house, where he would be at hand to supervise operations, at Bush Hill, near Edmonton. Later, while working the mines in Cardiganshire, he also had a house at Lodge Park,[3] overlooking the estuary of the Dovey; Lady Myddelton was with him there in September 1625,[4] but the likelihood is that he only paid periodical or occasional visits. Bush Hill, on the other hand, which with all its furniture and contents he left in his will to Lady Myddelton, must have been a more regular country residence, and while living there he accepted the office of trustee of the Latymer School at Edmonton, recently founded under the will of Edward Latymer.[5] It was at Bush Hill that Lady Myddelton spent her widowhood, and she was buried in Edmonton church. A description of Edmonton written early in the nineteenth century refers to 'a handsome villa' at Bush Hill, in which, though 'great alterations and improvements' had been made, 'some part of the old buildings' of Myddelton's house were still remaining.[6] The house on the site has since been enlarged and in great part rebuilt, and is now the Halliwick School for girl cripples, managed by the Church of England Children's Society.

Besides his own affairs as a business man and a landlord, and his major engineering works, Myddelton was also engaged from time to time on public duties both as a liveryman of the Goldsmiths' Company and as an expert on metallurgy. Towards the end of the sixteenth century a question arose about the 'coinage'

---

[1] Cf. below, p. 66.

[2] W. S. Prideaux, *Memorials of the Goldsmiths' Company*, i (1896), p. 121.

[3] Presumably rented: it belonged to Sir John Pryse of Gogerddan, and is not mentioned in Myddelton's will.

[4] Cf. below, p. 99.

[5] W. Wheatley, *History of Edward Latymer and his Foundations*, 2nd edn. (Beccles, 1953), p. 187.

[6] W. Robinson, *History and Antiquities of the Parish of Edmonton* (1819), p. 32.

of tin. Before being sold, all tin produced in the stannaries of Devon and Cornwall had to be taken, immediately after smelting, to one of the 'coinage towns' to be stamped and taxed. The pre-emption of tin was a royal prerogative, which hitherto had usually been farmed, but in 1599, after much discussion in the Privy Council, it was proposed that the Queen should take the pre-emption into her own hands, and in effect create a royal mono-poly of the metal. A 'Mr. Myddleton' was sent by the Government to the West of England to make inquiries in the stannaries; his christian name is not stated, but in view of his technical quali-fications, and of the mining work he subsequently undertook, it is tempting to surmise that it may have been our Hugh Myddelton to whom this mission was entrusted. It was said that the Queen would lose if she paid more than £25 a thousandweight, and it seems doubtful whether the proposal was adopted for more than a short time, if at all, for on 16 October Bevis Bulmer offered to pay her £10,000 a year for a lease of the right of pre-emption, at the same time undertaking to pay the tinners the price they had previously received, £26. 13s. 4d. a thousandweight.[1]

In 1599 Myddelton was one of a group of goldsmiths who had cause to complain to the Wardens about a certain George Lang-dale who kept a furnace in his cellar in Cheapside. The Wardens, 'considering the fearful danger threatened to the inhabitants in Goldsmiths' Row, through the untowardness of the place where the cellar is situate', summoned Langdale 'to make answer to the complaint', and on his refusing 'to remove the nuisance' he was committed to prison.[2] In 1611 Myddelton was concerned, together with a number of the Wardens and Assistants, in another disciplinary matter, when a member of the Court named Gosson was expelled for opposing the company at law and various other offences.[3] In 1622, when an inquiry came from the Privy Council about the wastage of silver, Hugh Myddelton was chosen, with five other members of the company, to assist the Wardens in

---

[1] H.M.C. *Cecil MSS.* ix. 426–7; *Cal. S.P.D. 1598–1601*, p. 330. Cf. G. R. Lewis, *The Stannaries* (Harvard, 1907), pp. 44–45, 145–6, and notes. The name of Bevis Bulmer is also of interest in this connexion: cf. below, p. 25.

[2] W. S. Prideaux, *Memorials of the Goldsmiths' Company*, i (1896), pp. 96–97.

[3] Ibid., p. 119.

preparing an answer; the paper they drafted stated seven reasons for the waste.[1]

The insolent pretensions of some of the hangers-on about the Court in the later years of James's reign are revealed by an affair of which Myddelton, who had access to Court circles, got wind. In 1624 he reported to the Goldsmiths' Company that a certain Mr. Manley 'of the Bedroom', and another courtier named Cotton, had moved 'a suit . . . to the king' with a view to getting the 'benefit of a composition' from the company (in other words, they tried to blackmail the company) 'on the pretence that the Wardens have incurred the penalty of *praemunire* by administering oaths for which they had no sufficient warrant'. The company thought that no oaths had been administered but such as were common to other companies, and that no blame therefore attached to the Wardens, but the Wardens were told to prepare a defence in case the matter were pressed to a trial at law.[2] By this time Myddelton was an elderly man, and in the previous year his eldest son received the freedom of the Goldsmiths' Company by patrimony. In the Court Minutes the space for his name is left blank and was never filled in. It was in fact Hugh; a possible explanation may be that he died before the freedom became effective.[3] The exact date of his death is unknown, but he must have predeceased his father, for it was the next son, William, who succeeded to his father's title.

In addition to all his other activities, Hugh Myddelton was M.P. for the borough of Denbigh, but his parliamentary career was undistinguished, and he does not appear to have taken part in the great political controversies of these years. He served on a number of committees, mostly concerned with commercial or financial questions, such as the committee on a Bill 'for Explanation of

---

1 W. S. Prideaux, *Memorials of the Goldsmiths' Company*, i (1896), p. 135.
2 Ibid., p. 139.
3 While he was the eldest then living, actually Hugh was the second son. The eldest, Thomas, baptized 28 Jan. 1599, died in infancy and was buried in St. Matthew's, Friday St., on 29 May 1600. Hugh was baptized at St. Matthew's on 20 Sept. 1601 (Registers of St. Matthew's, in *Harleian Soc.* lxiii (1933), pp. 11, 12). He is named in the charter of the New River Co., but the only other scrap of information about him is that on 10 Nov. 1623 he was granted a pass to travel 'into forraigne partes for three yeares with two servantes and provisions', but was 'not to goe to Rome' (*Acts P.C. June 1623–Mar. 1625*, p. 114). Possibly he never returned from this journey.

the Statute of Sewers', or a Bill 'for securing and confirming the lands, tenements and grants devised or conveyed to the several companies of the city of London', besides the committee on the Bill to authorize the construction of the New River.[1] His brother Robert, member for Weymouth, was also a member of these and other parliamentary committees, but, while the clerk sometimes distinguishes the brothers in the *Journals* by a christian name or an initial, unfortunately he often simply refers to both of them as 'Mr. Middleton'. In the first Parliament of James's reign 'a couple of dozen committees, four speeches, and one turn as teller are attributed to Robert, while Hugh is credited with only about fifteen committees and nothing else'. There are nearly twenty plain 'Mr. Middleton' entries, and it seems safer to attribute these to Robert than to Hugh, as he was generally the more assiduous parliamentarian, and had wider interests.[2]

Samuel Smiles and some other writers have ascribed to Hugh Myddelton a more conspicuous part in the Addled Parliament of 1614. Trouble developed in this Parliament over questions of supply, and in particular over the well-worn subject of impositions. The Government attempted to conciliate the malcontents by introducing certain 'Bills of Grace', but they refused to be bought off, and it was pointed out that the concessions offered benefited particular interests rather than the community as a whole. On 12 April 'Mr. Middleton' voiced the objections of the London merchants in a speech describing the Bills as tending 'to the Gentility, not to Cities, Burgesses, or Merchants', and he proposed instead a bill against impositions.[3] The speaker may conceivably have been Hugh;[4] but Robert, who in this Parliament sat for the City of London, again seems more likely. In the *Journals* for this Parliament Hugh is only once mentioned by name, and that simply as a member of a minor committee, whereas

---

[1] *C.J.* i. 262, 368. Cf. below, p. 29.
[2] I quote a letter to myself from Prof. A. H. Dodd. See also his 'Wales's Parliamentary Apprenticeship (1536–1625)', in *Trans. Soc. Cymmrodorion*, 1942 (1944), pp. 30, 31.
[3] *C.J.* i. 461.
[4] The latest author to attribute the speech to Hugh Myddelton is Williams M. Mitchell, *The Rise of the Revolutionary Party in the English House of Commons, 1603–29* (New York, 1957), p. 61. T. L. Moir, *The Addled Parliament* (Oxford, 1958), pp. 91, 101, assumes that the speaker was Robert.

Robert is specifically reported as having spoken so often that it seems reasonable to identify any unspecified Middleton with him.[1]

I think we must also abandon the idea that it was Hugh Myddelton who launched a spirited attack in the Commons, on 20 May 1614, on Alderman Cockayne's famous scheme, which had the King's backing, to prohibit the export of undressed and undyed cloth. The object of the scheme was to encourage the dressing and dyeing of cloth in England instead of in the Netherlands, and it was a damaging blow to the Merchant Adventurers, whose principal trade was exporting undressed cloth. A new company, called the King's Merchant Adventurers, was set up to implement the scheme, but the Netherlanders replied by placing an embargo upon the importation of all cloths, dressed or undressed, and the whole project eventually collapsed. 'Mr. Middleton', who endeavoured to enlist parliamentary support for the Merchant Adventurers' opposition to Cockayne's project, inveighed against the false pretensions of the new company: they were 'like watermen', looking one way and rowing another: a 'sepulcher, fair without, dead bones within'—the implication being that they would not seriously try to export only dyed and dressed cloths, but were really aiming at getting a share in the export of unfinished cloths. In practice, he declared, the project was 'infesible'. Alderman Cockayne might think it could be done 'with a Pen, or an Argument at Council Table', but the Merchant Adventurers knew it could not. He tried to arouse the sympathy of the House by stressing the unemployment the scheme would cause, and, citing his own case, declared that he and his partner maintained over 3,000 workmen, and paid the Exchequer over £20,000 a year in revenue.[2]

The speech failed to win over the Commons, where the Merchant Adventurers were far from popular, particularly among the members from the clothing counties, who believed that the company had an unfairly large share of the benefits of the cloth trade, and were pleased to see its monopoly broken. On

[1] Cf. A. H. Dodd in *Trans. Soc. Cymmrodorion*, 1942 (1944), p. 39.
[2] *C.J.* i. 491.

the whole it seems much more likely that Robert rather than Hugh Myddelton delivered this speech.[1] There is no other evidence that Hugh was concerned in any way with the cloth industry or trade, still less that he employed 3,000 workmen in it,[2] and it seems inherently improbable that a goldsmith, whose other known interests were in engineering projects, would have had either the inclination or the time for it. His brother Robert, on the other hand, apart from his greater parliamentary activity, was a merchant with varied interests in overseas trade; moreover, as M.P. for the City of London he would be a much more likely spokesman for the trading interests of the Merchant Adventurers than his brother who sat for a small Welsh borough. The notion that it was Hugh may have arisen from his description in the list of 'Aldermen and Capitall Burgesses' in the Denbigh borough register as 'Cittizen and Gouldsmith of London, and one of the Merchant Adventurers of England'. I think, however, that this last phrase should be interpreted in a general sense, as implying simply that he was an important personage 'in the City', as we might say. In Tudor and Stuart times any shareholder in a merchant company was called an 'Adventurer'—the partners in the New River were so called—and we need not regard it as evidence that he was actually a member of the Merchant Adventurers' Company.

One of the often-repeated legends about Hugh Myddelton is that in Queen Elizabeth's reign he used to sit smoking at the door of his house in the city with Sir Walter Raleigh, who introduced tobacco into England.[3] This may of course be true, for Thomas Myddelton had various dealings with Raleigh. As likely as not, however, it is another instance of mistaken identity, and Hugh's cousin, the sea-captain William Middleton, seems a more likely person to have been a pioneer of smoking than Hugh.[4] Naturally enough, Hugh served on the committee in the

---

[1] Cf. Astrid Friis, *Alderman Cockayne's Project and the Cloth Trade* (Copenhagen, 1927), pp. 25, n. 3, 254–6.
[2] The figure may well be a rhetorical exaggeration.
[3] J. P. Malcolm, *Anecdotes of the Manners and Customs of London* (quarto edn. 1811), p. 115.
[4] T. Pennant, *Tours in Wales* (1784), ii. 28.

Parliament of 1621 when the New River Company promoted a Bill for the confirmation of its powers,[1] and possibly on a few other committees as well, but otherwise he seems to have remained inconspicuous to the end of his parliamentary career. He had enough to occupy him as a business man and engineer, and in the following year there came well-deserved recognition of his achievements in these spheres.

Some years previously the King had adopted a suggestion of Robert Carr's, that there were many people who would be willing to pay considerable sums for the grant of a hereditary title, and that money raised in this way might be used to support the army then engaged in Ulster. The new title of baronet was accordingly created, which James offered to any knights or esquires, being persons of good repute and possessed of lands worth £1,000 a year, who were prepared to pay £1,080 in three annual instalments, the amount required to keep thirty infantry soldiers for three years. It was expected that 200 baronets would be created, and before the end of the reign that number had been made up, but at first applications came in only slowly.[2] On 19 October 1622 Hugh Myddelton was created a baronet, with the title of Sir Hugh Myddelton of Ruthin in the county of Denbigh;[3] but though the rank had been invented as a money-making device, to him it was granted as an honour. Special instructions were given that he was to be exempted from paying the customary charge,[4] and the grant was accompanied by a citation of his three notable accomplishments. These were:

1. For bringing to the city of London with excessive Charge and greater Difficulty, a new Cutt or River of fresh Water, to the great benefitt and inestimable preservation thereof.

2. For gaining a very great and spacious Quantity of Land in Brading Haven in the Isle of Wight, out of the Bowells of the Sea; and with Bankes and Pyles and most strange defensible and chargeable

---

[1] Cf. below, pp. 74, 75.

[2] Cf. *Parly. Hist.* v. 271, and S. R. Gardiner, *History of England 1603–42*, ii. 112.

[3] *47th Report of the Deputy Keeper of the Public Records* (1886), p. 130; *Patent Roll* [no. 2271] 20 *James I*, p. 3, no. 22.

[4] B.M. Sloane MSS. ii. 4177, f. 220. According to Gardiner the usual charge was £1,080, but the sum mentioned in Myddelton's case was £1,095. I suppose the difference may represent a commission or fee to Exchequer officials.

Mountaines, fortifying the same against the violence and fury of the Waves.

3. For finding out, with fortunate and prosperous Skill, exceeding Industry, and noe small Charge, in the County of Cardigan, a royall and rich Myne, from whence he hath extracted many Silver Plates which have been coyned in the Tower of London for currant Money of England.[1]

It has sometimes been said that he was 'knight and baronet', and that he was knighted in 1613 on the occasion of the opening ceremony at New River Head, but this is erroneous. In his will he described himself simply as 'baronet', and he remained 'Mr. Myddelton', or 'Hugh Myddelton, citizen and goldsmith of London', until the baronetcy was conferred in 1622. His arms were 'Quarterly of four, first and fourth argent, on a bend vert three wolves' heads erased of the field', with the motto *Omnia ex Deo, mentem non munus*. On being made a baronet he applied to William Camden, Clarenceux King of Arms, for an alteration of his arms,[2] placing the three wolves' heads on a pile instead of on a bend. His coat of arms as a baronet appears on his portrait, surmounted by a hand, and with the motto *Virtus palma*. The wolves' heads were in allusion to his family's descent from Rhirid Flaidd (or Blaidd, meaning a wolf). The hand, which is a feature of all the Myddelton arms, and resembles the hand of Ulster, is said to indicate the glove trade that formerly flourished at Denbigh. It can be seen repeated many times on the carved oak staircase in the Bull Hotel there.

Meanwhile Myddelton was always willing to lend a hand in any Welsh business that he thought deserved his support. A minor instance occurred in 1624, when it was proposed to grant the Greenwax of Wales[3] to Sir Richard Wynn, one of the sons of Sir John Wynn of Gwydir. Sir Eubule Thelwall[4] got up a petition to the Prince of Wales against it, on the ground that such a grant never had been and ought not to be made to a subject.

---

[1] B.M. Harleian MSS., no. 1507, art. 40 (Catalogue, ii. 84*b*).

[2] W. M. Myddelton, *Pedigree of the Family of Myddelton* (Horncastle, 1910), p. 18; Harleian MSS., loc. cit.

[3] An office concerned with the issue to sheriffs of documents from the Exchequer.

[4] Cf. below, p. 90.

Hugh Myddelton was one of fifteen signatories to this petition, but we gather that its only effect was to cause Sir Richard some trouble, and he obtained his lease in the end.[1]

It was in this year that Myddelton served his second term as Prime Warden of the Goldsmiths' Company. During the year the company had cause to complain of the 'obstinate demeanor towards them' of a certain Thomas Clowse, and he was committed to the Fleet prison until he 'should make his submission at their hall'. This he duly made, and it was on Sir Hugh's certificate that he had done so that he was released.[2] About this time Sir Hugh's services were in frequent demand. In 1629 he was a member of a committee appointed by the Court of the Goldsmiths' Company 'to peruse the Company's book of wills' and make sure that the various benefactions bequeathed to the company were being administered in accordance with the donors' wishes.[3] The Government also sought his assistance on more than one occasion. Three years before this, the Privy Council had instructed him, together with a body of other experts, headed by Sir Robert Cotton, to 'meete and conferr together' on some question concerning the Mint, and to make a written report to the Council.[4] Another piece of government service came early in 1630, when a commission was set up 'to inquire into exacted fees and offices innovated' since the eleventh year of Queen Elizabeth's reign. The commission contained twenty-two members, headed by the Lord President of the Council, the Lord Privy Seal, the Earl Marshal, and several peers. Further down the list, alongside well-known names such as Sir Robert Cotton and Sir Henry Spelman, were the two brothers Sir Hugh and Sir Thomas Myddelton.[5] One suspects that what lay behind this was a hope on the King's part to raise money by creating new offices or raising the fees for old ones.

This must have been one of the last occasions on which the two brothers were associated. Next year they both died, Thomas on

[1] N.L.W. Cal. Wynn Papers, nos. 1217, 1228.
[2] Acts P.C., June 1623–Mar. 1625, p. 283 (24 July 1624).
[3] W. S. Prideaux, Memorials of the Goldsmiths' Company, i (1896), p. 149.
[4] Acts P.C. June–Dec. 1626, pp. 240–1 (31 Aug. 1626).
[5] Cal. S.P.D., 1629–31, pp. 179, 236.

12 August, aged about 81, Hugh, who was about ten years younger, on 7 December.[1] Throughout his life in London, Hugh had been a worshipper at St. Matthew's, Friday Street, and he served as churchwarden in 1598–9 and 1599–1600.[2] It was there that six of his sons and five of his daughters were baptized, and his first wife and several of his children who died young (including his eldest son) were buried. Now he was buried there himself, on 10 December 1631.[3] In his will he directed that a monument should be erected there to his memory, but the church was destroyed in the Great Fire of 1666, and the monument perished with it. The church was rebuilt by Wren in 1685, but it was finally demolished in 1883, and the remains of those buried there were then removed and 'decently interred' in Ilford Cemetery.[4] On this occasion the New River Company made inquiries about the site of Sir Hugh's grave, and the workmen were offered a reward if they could find any trace of his coffin or memorial, but nothing was found.[5]

[1] B.M. Sloane MSS. 866 (Richard Smith's Obituary). This also records the deaths of Sir Thomas Myddelton and of William Lewyn, the clerk to the New River Co. Cf. Francis Peck, *Desiderata Curiosa*, ii. 524.

[2] Churchwardens' Accounts of St. Matthew's, now in the Guildhall Library. He also audited the accounts for several years.

[3] Registers of St. Matthew's (*Harleian Soc.* lxiii (1933), p. 123).

[4] W. Duncombe Pink, *Notes on the Middleton Family* (Chester, 1891), p. 38.

[5] Note by W. Sparrow Simpson, Rector of St. Matthew's, in *N. & Q.*, 7th series, iii (1887), p. 478.

II

THE GENESIS OF THE NEW RIVER

THE story of London's water-supply has often been told.[1] In the Middle Ages, apart from wells and springs, the Thames and its tributaries were the main sources, and water was brought from the river in carts, or in buckets by water-carriers. The supply of piped water to individual houses lay in the future, but the city had a number of public fountains, called conduits, which were supplied with water brought in lead pipes from springs in outlying suburbs. As the population grew, new conduits were erected in several places (ultimately there were sixteen), but the wells and springs became contaminated or began to dry up, and could not keep pace with the increasing demand. What was in principle an important new step, even if in practice it proved ineffective, was taken in 1544, when the mayor and commonalty of the city were empowered by Act of Parliament[2] to bring water to the city from springs at Hampstead. According to Scott, this was the first private Act of Parliament giving a local authority compulsory powers to enter privately owned land and lay pipes, providing for compensation, and prescribing penalties for resistance to the corporation's servants.[3] Apart from an unsuccessful attempt in 1589,[4] however, the powers conferred by the act of 1544 do not seem to have been exercised, and it was not until late in the seventeenth century that a company (subsequently called the Hampstead Aqueducts) was promoted to utilize these sources of supply. Schemes for making more water available to Londoners in the later sixteenth century all involved recourse once more to the Thames. One of the most ambitious of these schemes was carried out by the Dutchman (or German) Peter Morris (or Morice), who in 1581 was granted a

---

[1] See Note on Sources, p. xi.   [2] 35 Henry VIII, c. 10
[3] W. R. Scott, *Joint Stock Companies*, iii. 4.
[4] J. Stow, *Survey of London* (ed. C. L. Kingsford, Oxford, 1908), i. 13.

lease for 500 years of the first arch of London Bridge, in which he erected a waterwheel, driven by the tide, to pump up water from the river. Morris's waterworks mark another important step, for his water was conveyed through lead pipes laid in the streets to individual houses in the neighbourhood,[1] and he was so successful that he obtained a loan of £1,000 from the city, and a year later was granted a lease of the second arch as well. His undertaking, which became known as the London Bridge Water-works, lasted until 1822, not long before old London Bridge itself was taken down.

Another personality of some interest in the history of London's water in Elizabethan times was Bevis Bulmer, who was a man of versatile talents and, like Hugh Myddelton after him, achieved success as a mining engineer.[2] In 1593 he obtained a lease from the corporation entitling him to erect a pump worked by horses at Broken Wharf, not far from St. Paul's, to supply the western part of the city. Additional conduits were also erected, two of which were supplied with Thames water from Morris's machine; some years previously another, called Dowgate Conduit, was supplied by a horse-pump on the river-bank. About the same time an Italian engineer named Gianibelli obtained official approval for a waterworks scheme at Tyburn, but this and other schemes in the later years of Queen Elizabeth's reign were all on a relatively small scale.

Thames water, while practically unlimited in amount, could not, with the pumping machinery then available, be carried any great distance from the river; also, with the growth of London,[3] quantities of filth and refuse of all kinds were thrown into the river,[4] in spite of efforts to prohibit the practice, and the water inevitably must have been far from pure. The superintendent of the London Bridge Waterworks in later years declared that after

---

[1] City Records (Guildhall), Repertories 20, f. 201; R. Holinshed, *Chronicles*, iv (1808 edn.), p. 496.   [2] See *N. & Q.*, 11th series, iv (1911), pp. 401–3.

[3] For estimates of the population of London see N. G. Brett-James, *The Growth of Stuart London* (1935), c. xx. Early in the seventeenth century the city and liberties had perhaps 130,000 inhabitants; 'Greater London', i.e. including also the outer wards and parishes, together with Westminster, Stepney, Lambeth, etc., 'perhaps 250,000'.

[4] There were complaints of the pollution of the Thames from the fourteenth century onwards (F. Clifford, *Private Bill Legislation*, ii. 45).

it had stood in a cistern for twenty-four hours it was 'as fine and clear as could be imagined',[1] but in spite of such reassurances fresh spring water, such as used to be supplied by the conduits, must obviously have been preferable. Londoners could only have this if it were brought in from outside, and in the sixteenth century London was relatively behind-hand in this respect in comparison with some other towns. The streets of Tiverton, for example, had been supplied with water by a leat, or artificial channel, since the thirteenth century. More recent, and famous because of the prominent part played in promoting it by Sir Francis Drake, was the public water supply at another Devonshire town, Plymouth. The purpose of this was not to take water to individual houses, but to water ships and scour out the harbour, and to serve as a precaution in cases of fire, though it also fed some public conduits. The Plymouth Leat, or Drake's Leat as it is sometimes called, is an open channel, some six or seven feet wide; and though its source, a dam on the River Meavy on Dartmoor, is only ten miles from Plymouth, its winding course, followed in order to maintain a gentle incline, is about eighteen miles in length. Completed in 1591, it thus resembled the future New River on a small scale, and its construction may indeed have stimulated projects, already being talked about, for bringing water to London from the neighbouring countryside. The corporation had obtained an Act of Parliament in 1571 for making 'a new cut or trench' from 'the river of Lee',[2] but this had nothing to do with the supply of water. The New Cut, or Barge River as it was sometimes called when later on it came to be made, was intended to improve navigation between Ware and London for the carriage of 'victuals, corn and other necessaries', by cutting out some of the windings of the Lea, and it is not to be confused with Myddelton's river.[3] Apart from this, however, there were several proposals to tap either the Lea or alternatively the Colne for supplying water to London. In 1580 a man named Russell

[1] R. Sisley, *The London Water Supply*, p. 7. This was in 1821, just before the end of the London Bridge Waterworks.

[2] 13 Eliz. I, c. 18.

[3] F. Clifford, op. cit. ii. 55. See also G. B. G. Bull, 'Elizabethan Maps of the Lower Lea Valley', in *Geographical Journal*, vol. 124 (1958), pp. 375–8, and H. Chauncy, *The*

propounded to Burleigh a scheme for drawing water from the 'River of Uxbridge', and 'by a geometrical instrument' he showed that the levels were such that 'with discreet leading' the water would flow to London by gravitation.[1] Burleigh was interested in this scheme, but again nothing seems to have been done. No doubt the chief reason why these and other proposals were never put into effect was that neither the city nor any other authorities were willing to undertake the expense of what seemed to them a large and difficult task, and they thought it more prudent and appropriate to leave such ventures to private enterprise.

At length, about the end of the sixteenth century, Edmund Colthurst, of Bath, put forward a proposal to tap certain springs in Hertfordshire and Middlesex. Colthurst had recently seen military service in Ireland, where he had defended a castle in County Waterford,[2] and he is often referred to as Captain Colthurst; but perhaps his chief claim to be remembered (besides his part in planning the New River) was that it was he who gave the abbey church, which had fallen into ruin since the dissolution of the monasteries, to the mayor and citizens of Bath.[3] Colthurst's proposal was referred to the authorities of the City of London, and to the sheriffs of Hertfordshire and Middlesex, who, after local inquiries, approved it subject to certain conditions. Finally, on 18 April 1604, James I granted Colthurst a licence by letters patent[4] to dig a river not more than six feet wide, provided it was completed within seven years. The King was to be paid a rent of £20 per annum once the river began to show a profit: two-thirds

Historical Antiquities of Hertfordshire (1700), p. 4. This confusion existed as early as 1606, when the city's failure to exercise the powers conferred by the act of 1571 was urged as an objection to the Bill authorizing the construction of the New River (*Parly. Diary of Robert Bowyer*, ed. D. H. Willson (Minneapolis, 1931), p. 176).

[1] J. Stow, *Survey of the Cities of London and Westminster* (ed. John Strype, 1720), i. 27.

[2] H.M.C. *Cecil MSS.* xiv. 157.

[3] His father had bought the abbey from the man who acquired it at the Dissolution; the 'abbey-house, with the park called Prior's Park' and other properties, were sold. After Colthurst gave it to the city, the church was repaired with the help of various benefactors, and it is interesting, in view of his connexion with the New River, to read that the west door was 'beautified' in 1617 by Sir Henry Montagu, whose brother was Bishop of Bath and Wells (J. Collinson, *History of Somerset* (1791), i. 57–59).

[4] Patent Roll, 2 James I, part 25. The original is in the possession of the Metropolitan Water Board. Cf. also H.M.C. *Cecil MSS.* xvii. 181, and *Cal. S.P.D. 1603–10*, p. 93.

of the water was to be used for cleansing 'the Tower Ditch, the Fleet Ditch and all other ditches by the city walls', while the remaining third would be supplied to houses in London and Westminster. One of the possible sources Colthurst may have had in mind for his river was the Chadwell spring, which rose in the Lea valley a short distance above Ware; a couple of miles or so down stream additional water could be drawn from another spring, said to be named after Queen Emma, Canute's wife, which rose below the church at Great Amwell. Colthurst mentioned 'springs towards Hertford', but he also probably intended to tap some other springs on the way to London, such as one, described as 'a plentiful spring', which had been found near the 'new lodge' at Theobalds.[1] Theobalds, near Enfield, then belonged to the Cecil family, though it was afterwards acquired by James I in exchange for Hatfield, and the preliminary stages of Colthurst's plans involved him in correspondence and negotiations with Robert Cecil, since the route to London went through Cecil's property. Cecil, we gather, believed that the scheme was impossible, but Colthurst was confident of success;[2] so much so, in fact, that a couple of years later, after the grant of his patent, when he asked Viscount Cranborne for leave to cut through Theobalds Park, and was advised 'to join with him some artist and try the levels before he troubles the country', he refused, 'and says he will have the honour hereof himself. If it prevail not, he will bear the loss and shame'.[3] Places mentioned on the line of route—Broxbourne, Wormley, Cheshunt, and Edmonton—make it clear that Colthurst was the real originator of the idea of the New River, but he did not get far with it before he found himself in difficulties. Early in 1605 he said he had brought the river forward three miles, at a cost of over £200, and he sought to enlist Cranborne's support in trying to persuade the Lord Mayor and aldermen to contribute to the expense.[4] He also got

[1] Cf. H.M.C. *Cecil MSS.* xii. 370, xvi. 55.

[2] Cf. his letter to Cecil dated 23 July 1602, ibid., p. 242.

[3] H.M.C. *Cecil MSS.* xvii. 181. Robert Cecil (Burghley's second son) was made Viscount Cranborne on 20 Aug. 1604 and 1st Earl of Salisbury on 4 May 1605. From a comment (ibid.) on Colthurst's petition by Mr. Israel Amice (Cranborne's steward, presumably) it looks as if there were already a New River of some kind at Theobalds.

[4] Ibid.

the Privy Council to address a minute, in which the city authorities were reminded of the benefits of 'cleansing the ditches and other unwholesome places, the enormity whereof is known to be very great', and were told that the Privy Council 'esteem it very reasonable' that they should bear part of the cost.[1]

Meanwhile, however, other schemes were in the air. The Common Council appointed a committee to consider proposals to bring water 'either from the Ryvers of Uxbridge, Lee, or from Amwell or any other places thereabouts',[2] the outcome of which was the promotion of a Bill in Parliament to cover alternative sources of supply. It received its first reading in the Commons on 30 January 1606, and was described as 'the Bill for the bringing in of a fresh stream of water from the River of Lee, or Uxbridge, to the north parts of the city of London'.[3] Thereupon Colthurst, who meanwhile had gone off to Cambridge, 'bringing a river there', wrote to Cecil protesting that this would ruin his prospects, and he stressed the damage it would cause to 'the king's mills standing on Uxbridge river; and the Thames, which is already hard to pass with barges for want of water, will be much worse'. He now declared that he had spent £700 on the first three miles of his river,[4] and begged Cecil to use his influence 'to stay the bill; or that it be provided that none of the Uxbridge river shall be put into the pipe, but employed for navigation, . . . so that he may enjoy the whole benefit of his water by putting it into pipes'.[5] Presumably as a result of his protests, Colthurst was invited to come and 'be heard' at the committee stage of the

[1] H.M.C. *Cecil MSS.* xvi. 417. The Court of Aldermen appointed a committee to consider the Privy Council's letter. It included Hugh Myddelton's brother Sir Thomas (City Records, Repertories 26/2, f. 515 verso).

[2] City Records, Journals 26, f. 392.

[3] *C.J.* i. 261. The spellings 'Lee' and 'Lea' have long been alternatives. 'Lea' seems to be the commoner nowadays, and is adopted by the Ordnance Survey, but the poet Spenser spelt it 'Lee', and this is the statutory spelling retained by the Metropolitan Water Board.

[4] Estimates of Colthurst's expenditure grew rapidly. A paper headed 'The state of the cause concerninge the water works' (Bodl. Tanner MSS. 98, f. 113), drawn up at the time of the hold-up in 1610–11, says that he 'laid out about £1000 . . . and did bringe the said streame two miles or thereabouts', but this included the cost of obtaining his patent as well as making the river.

[5] H.M.C. *Cecil MSS.* xvi. 55. In the H.M.C. Report this letter is dated '? 1604, 11 April', but I think the year should probably be 1606, as it was in the spring of that year that the corporation's Bill was before Parliament.

Bill,[1] and he seems to have succeeded in persuading the promoters to buy what was substantially his scheme. At the third reading 'Mr. Recorder, in the name of the Lord Mayor and the State of the City . . . promised, that they will submit themselves to such order, for recompense to be given to Capt. Colthirst, as the Lord Chancellor shall set down'.[2] The Bill was then carried, on 20 May 1606, but only against substantial opposition (the votes were 60 to 49) in a half-empty house, which is significant in view of the concerted hostility organized later while the river was in course of construction. During the debate, apart from Colthurst's claims, Sir William Stroude brought up objections based on experience of the leat at Plymouth, into which, he alleged, 'the Cittizens do cast all the soyle and filth of the Citty, and sweepe the Streets into it after raine, that the same running into the Haven, doth make great Obstructions there'. He feared the same would happen with the Thames if the New River were made, but, we are told, 'this reason moved not'.[3] The Bill was then sent up to the Lords 'with this message: that some recompense may be considered by the City to Capt. Colthirst', and went through all its stages there with great rapidity. At its third reading, on 26 May, the question of compensation for Colthurst was further discussed, and the House resolved 'that stay should be made . . . by the . . . Lord Chancellor for granting any commission under the Great Seal of England (upon any matter concerning that Bill)[4] until such recompense should be made unto the said Colthurst, for his travail and pains in the aforesaid work, as his Lordship should think reasonable'.[5] As finally passed, 'the River of Lee, or Uxbridge' disappeared from the title, and the Bill was simply called 'An Act for the bringing in of a fresh Stream of running Water to the North Parts of the City of London'.[6]

The preamble states briefly that 'it is found very convenient and necessary to have a fresh Stream of running Water . . . brought to the North Parts of the City of London, from the

---

[1] *C.J.* i. 262.   [2] *C.J.* i. 310, 311.
[3] *Parly. Diary of Robert Bowyer* (ed. D. H. Willson), p. 176.
[4] This refers to the clause about settling compensation to landowners; see below, pp. 31 and 39.
[5] *L.J.* ii. 442.   [6] 3 James I, c. 18.

Springs of Chadwell and Amwell, and other Springs in the County of Hertford not far distant from the same, which upon view is found very feasible, and like to be profitable to many'. It is then enacted that the Lord Mayor, Commonalty, and Citizens of London shall have power 'at any time or times hereafter' to lay out 'such convenient Limits of ground for the making of the Trench for the said River at the breadth of ten Foot and not above', and to take and use the ground necessary for this purpose, to dig the ground 'alongst all the said whole length of the said River or New Cut', and 'for ever to maintain and preserve the same, and to lay the Earth there digged or to be digged on either side of the same River or New Cut, in such places as shall be thought meet for that purpose, and to have free passage to and from the said New Cut or River with Men, Horses, Carts and Carriages at all Times convenient, and in Places convenient, for making of the same New Cut or Trench and for the preserving of the same . . .'. The city authorities were to 'make satisfaction or Composition to and with the Lords, Owners and Occupiers of the . . . Grounds through which the New Cut or River shall be made, and with all such Person and Persons as shall sustain any Damage, Loss or Hindrance in their Mills standing upon any of the Rivers or Streams from which the Water shall be taken . . .'. Failing 'Agreement by mutual Assent', compensation was to be settled by commissioners appointed for the purpose by the Lord Chancellor or the Lord Keeper of the Great Seal. There were to be sixteen commissioners (four each from the counties of Middlesex, Essex, and Herts, and from the City of London) 'having Lands and Tenements of the clear yearly value of forty Pounds at the least': nine (to include two from the city) were to have power to act. In the event of 'Breaches, Inundations or Hurts', the city authorities should 'from time to time stop the Breaches at their own Charges, and sufficiently maintain them from Time to Time, and make sufficient Recompence to the Party grieved for the Damage sustained . . .'. They were also 'to make and maintain at their Costs and Charges from Time to Time convenient Bridges and Ways for the Passage of the King's subjects, and their Cattle and Carriages, over or through the said

New Cut or River, in Places meet or convenient'. A proviso which later proved the cause of considerable delay laid it down that nothing was to be done until either full agreement had been reached with the owners and occupiers, or orders for compensation had been decided by the commissioners. When completed the river was to be 'subject to the Commission of Sewers', but the city authorities were to bear the cost of 'all such things as shall be done at any time hereafter for the scouring, cleansing, amending and conservation of the said New River or Cut', while in return the city should receive the benefit of any fines imposed by the Commission of Sewers for 'any wilful annoyances and offences . . . to the hurt or prejudice of the river'.

No further construction seems to have been done for a couple of years or so, but 'Mr. Richard Staper, Clothworker', went on behalf of the city to inspect 'the springs of Almwell and Chaldwell' and survey 'the course how the same maye be brought to London', and was paid his expenses, which amounted to £5. 6s.[1] Meanwhile a new proposal was put forward by an expert on land drainage, named William Ingelbert, who apparently had been engaged on the city's behalf in the promotion of their Bill. He suggested that 'for the sweete keepeinge thereof',[2] and to lessen the damage to the ground, the water should be 'brought and conveyed in and through a trunk or vault of brick or stone inclosed, and in some places where need is, raised upon arches', instead of in an 'open trench or sewer'. Ingelbert evidently persuaded the city authorities that his scheme was preferable to Colthurst's,[3] and as it was doubtful whether the original Act would give the necessary powers, a second Act was obtained, expressly authorizing the construction of a closed channel.[4] This, however, would undoubtedly have been much more expensive than an open watercourse, and whether for this or for some other reason no more was heard of it. Ingelbert probably had a grievance, on which he enlarged to sympathetic listeners, for Aubrey records that his learned friend Fabian Philipps, who saw Ingelbert afterwards 'in a poore Rug-gowne like an Almes-man, sitting by an

---

[1] City Records, Repertories 27, f. 263.   [2] City Records, Journals 27, f. 89.
[3] Repertories 27, f. 263.   [4] 4 James I, c. 12.

apple-woman at the Parliament-stayres', told him that Ingelbert was 'the first Inventer or Projector of bringing the water from Ware to London called Middleton's water', for which he deserved a statue, whereas Myddelton, who 'moneyed the business' (and whom, incidentally, he calls an alderman of London), got the credit for it.[1] It is true that Myddelton has had the credit (and the statue), but, as we shall see, he did not take what was not due to him; and in any case none was due to Ingelbert.

It has usually been said that the city authorities were anxious to improve their water-supply, but would not pay anything and could not find anybody to undertake the work, until Myddelton generously stepped forward and offered to carry it out at his own expense.[2] This is only partly true. The corporation undoubtedly were unwilling to shoulder any responsibility themselves,[3] but it seems clear that Colthurst was willing enough, indeed anxious, to undertake the task, though he lacked the necessary resources. In October 1608, however, in a petition to the Court of Aldermen, he declared that he had friends and partners who were prepared to make the river at their own expense under the powers granted him by letters patent in 1604, but he wanted to be assured that the city authorities would not use the powers they now had by Act of Parliament to prevent him and his partners taking water from the springs at Chadwell and Amwell. On 28 October the Court agreed not to interfere with Colthurst's plans, but told him he must complete the work within two years of the following Lady Day, and made it clear that he must not expect any financial help from the city.[4] Colthurst and his friends apparently remained inactive during the winter, and in the meantime came to the conclusion that it would be desirable to have

---

[1] J. Aubrey, *Brief Lives* (ed. A. Clark, Oxford, 1898), ii. 1.

[2] Thus Anthony Munday, the continuator of Stow, says that 'when all else refused, Mr. Middleton undertook it' (*Survey of . . . London and Westminster*, ed. Strype, i. 26). Similarly Pennant remarks that 'no one was found bold enough to attempt it' until 'the dauntless WELSHMAN stept forth, and SMOTE THE ROCK' (T. Pennant, *Tours in Wales* (1784), ii. 29).

[3] Earlier they had granted loans of £1,000 each to Peter Morris and Bevis Bulmer, but these were definite sums. What they would not undertake was an unlimited liability for what no doubt seemed a formidable and risky venture. Later they made a definite loan of £3,000 to Myddelton (below, p. 65).

[4] Repertories 28, f. 288.

the city's powers transferred to themselves. The city's Act of 1606 allowed for a river ten feet wide, as against the maximum of six feet permitted by the letters patent of 1604, and another advantage of the Act was that it laid down a procedure for settling questions of compensation. Accordingly, on 7 March 1609, Colthurst made a fresh proposal, or rather two alternative proposals. He asked that the city should make over to him and his partners the benefits of their Acts, on condition that the river was brought to Islington within two years, and that then the corporation should pay £2,400,[1] in return for which two-thirds of the water should be allocated for public use. Alternatively, he and his partners would bear the whole cost on condition that they took the whole of the profits. The committee to which these proposals were referred were willing to give Colthurst the benefit of the Acts, but not to undertake any financial liability, and on 14 March they reported accordingly in favour of his second alternative. At the same time, while aware that he lacked the necessary means himself, they noted that he had 'taken unto him persons of good sufficiencie' to undertake the work.[2] One would expect, therefore, that the Common Council, which considered this report from their committee, would have authorized Colthurst, or Colthurst and his partners, to exercise the city's statutory powers. Instead, on 28 March 1609, without mentioning Colthurst, they accepted an offer by Hugh Myddelton, citizen and goldsmith of London, 'to undertake the same worke'. He promised to begin it within two months, and to 'doe his best endevour to finish the same within fower yeares', and accordingly they appointed him, his heirs and assigns, as the city's 'lawfull deputies, attorneys and agents'.[3] This appointment was followed by a formal agreement between Myddelton and the city authorities, drawn up by Sir Henry Montagu, the Recorder, and executed on 21 April 1609.[4]

How Myddelton first became interested and involved in the

---

[1] As Mr. Berry has remarked, it looks as if this figure represented two-thirds of the estimated cost of the river, so that 'it is not surprising that financial difficulties were encountered'. He also points out that this is the first mention in the records of Islington as the destination of the river.

[2] Repertories 29, f. 3.   [3] Journals 27, ff. 377 verso, 378.

[4] R. R. Sharpe, *London and the Kingdom* (1894), ii. 21.

question of London's water-supply is uncertain. He was a Member of Parliament when the Corporation's Bill was introduced in 1606, and he served on the committee which considered the Bill after its second reading in the Commons. So also, it is interesting to notice, did his brother Robert, and three others—Mr. Lawrence Hyde, Mr. Bacchus (Backhouse), and Mr. Recorder of London (Sir Henry Montagu)—all of whom later were among the original 'adventurers' in the New River Company. It seems likely that these and possibly others were the 'persons of good sufficiency' whose support Colthurst had already enlisted, and the probability is that, when a definite agreement was to be drawn up, the city authorities, or possibly the partners themselves, came to the conclusion that it would be preferable for the city's powers to be exercised by a man of substance, like Myddelton, rather than by Colthurst, who had no resources of his own.

It is possible that Myddelton had known something of Colthurst before serving on the parliamentary committee in 1606, for Colthurst evidently had some reputation as an expert on 'waterworks'. Rowland Vaughan, who wrote a curious account of irrigation works he had constructed on his estate in Herefordshire, tells us that 'being requested by many Gentlemen of the best quality to putt these Waterworkes in Print', he 'praied those ingenious Gentlemen (Sergeant Lovell and maister Coulthurst) to speake what they thought concerning the same', and they had replied encouragingly.[1] Furthermore, this was not the first contact between a Middleton and a Colthurst. One of the ships in the East India Company's expedition to the Moluccas in 1604, the leadership of which was entrusted to Sir Henry Middleton, who may have been a cousin of Hugh's, was commanded by a Christopher Colthurst.[2]

Many of the earlier accounts of the making of the New River are incomplete and inaccurate, particularly as regards its finances, and it has been pleaded that definite evidence is lacking, because a fire at the New River Company's offices in 1769 destroyed its

---

[1] R. Vaughan, *Most Approved and Long Experienced Waterworkes* (1610; reprinted with introd. by Ellen Beatrice Wood, 1897), p. 142.

[2] Hakluyt Soc., 2nd series, no. lxxxviii (1943), pp. xv, xvi.

early archives. Actually a few survived the fire, and are now in the custody of the Metropolitan Water Board. They include some remnants of the minutes of meetings, charred but partly legible, and nearly 300 receipts for compensation paid to landowners on the course of the river. By far the most valuable evidence, however, consists of nine account books now in the Public Record Office.[1] The purpose of these was to provide a detailed and certified warrant for the expenses, when James I agreed to pay half the cost of the river in return for half the profits, and they were kept up until 30 September 1632, by which time the Crown had given up its direct interest in the conduct of the undertaking. Apart from a few entries of sums received, they are mainly a record of disbursements, and include all wages and allowances paid, with the names of the workmen and other employees, particulars of the amounts spent on various sorts of materials, and numerous miscellaneous expenses, so that they give a detailed picture not only of the construction of the river but also of its maintenance after completion.

The first page of the first book opens with the heading in Myddelton's own hand: 'Mo[nie]s paid and Dysbursed for the bringinge of watter from the springs of Chadwell and Amwell to the Citty of london begonne this 20th of Februarie 1608 [i.e. 1609] as followeth'. This date does not mean that the actual work of construction began then (apart from Colthurst's work on the first three miles of the river), for the initial entries refer to legal charges (25 March: 'To Mr.Recorder for his fee in that busenes', £2) and such items as 11s. 7d. 'that was spent at Walt[h]am for hors hier upon the first surveye'. But the date 20 February, over a month before Myddelton's appointment as the city's deputy, and the first two items after the heading—'To Mr. Stonne for his counsell in my booke from the Citty at twis', £1, and 'To Mr. Coulthurst to geve the oficer for warnynge the Comitty to meate in that busenes', 2s. 6d.—make it clear that Myddelton was already in partnership with Colthurst during the negotiations that culminated in the transfer of the city's powers to Myddelton, and later items show that Colthurst by no means dropped out of

[1] See Note on Sources, p. xi.

the venture when Myddelton was appointed to manage it. On 29 March Colthurst was paid £10, and various sums were advanced to him for paying wages: the first of these, on 5 May 1609, may indicate the date when work actually started, for on the same day £2. 18s. was paid to William Parnell for 600 'of bords for the springe headd and for the caredge therof'. From 2 August Colthurst received a regular weekly allowance of 14s.,[1] which, except for an interruption during the great hold-up in 1610–11,[2] went on until August 1616, when he probably died. In the pageant at the opening ceremony at New River Head he came first, as 'the Overseer'. Though Colthurst's contribution to the venture has been overshadowed by Myddelton's, Sir Hugh himself was far from unmindful of what it owed to Colthurst, and he arranged that a life-interest in four of the thirty-six Adventurers' shares should be assigned to 'Edmund Colthurst of the Cittie of Bathe gent. in consideracon of great labour and endeavour by him bestowed about the said worke'.[3]

[1] On 9 Sept. 1609 the wages were 16s. 'To Mr. Colthurst and his boye'. The boy's wages appear each week until 14 Oct. (except that on 30 Sept. the entry is 'To Mr. Colthurst for his twoe weeks wages and one for his boye' £1. 10s.); from 21 Oct. Colthurst drew 14s. for himself only.

[2] See below, p. 39. He was paid 14s. on 9 June 1610, but on 16 June the item 'Mr. Colthurste his wages' is struck out. His wages (14s.) began again on 12 Oct. 1611.

[3] After Colthurst's death, his heirs were to have two of the shares, the other two going to Myddelton. This was arranged at the time of the conveyance, by a deed dated 8 May 1612 (now at the offices of the Metropolitan Water Board) of two shares to one of the Adventurers, Sir Henry Nevill, of Billingsbear Park, Berks. He was to receive two-thirty-sixths, i.e. one-eighteenth, of the profits, but was to contribute one-sixteenth of the expenditure, because Colthurst was to get his shares free of charge. As the city's deputy Myddelton, of course, was obliged in any case to compensate Colthurst; the fact that they had become partners enabled him to do so more easily by a grant of shares.

III

THE MAKING OF THE RIVER

AFTER the preliminary items of expenditure already mentioned, the seventh entry in the New River accounts, dated 5 May 1609, is 'To Mr. Wright for his 3 sevāll surveis to Amwell and back againe to Islington', £20. 3s. This was the celebrated mathematician Edward Wright, of Garveston, Norfolk, formerly a sizar and later a fellow of Gonville and Caius College, Cambridge,[1] who translated Napier's work on logarithms into English, and in his *Certain Errors in Navigation*, published in 1599, demonstrated the mathematical principles by which charts could be constructed on Mercator's projection. Wright had already been concerned with London's water-supply, for in 1600 he borrowed £200 from the corporation free of interest in connexion with a scheme for taking water from the Thames to supply Leadenhall and adjacent parts of the city.[2] I do not know whether this was how Myddelton came to make his acquaintance and choose him as his surveyor; at any rate he was soon established in regular employment as the expert to plot the river's course. A week later the accounts contain the entry: 'Paid to Mr. Wright before hande to be my Arts man' £40, presumably a proportion of his salary paid in advance to secure his services; then from 9 September he received a weekly allowance of £2.

On 10 July 1609 the Lord Mayor wrote to the Privy Council, saying that Mr. Hugh Myddelton, goldsmith, had undertaken, as the city's deputy, to carry out the work of bringing a fresh stream of running water from the springs of Chadwell and Amwell to the north parts of the city, and requesting the

---

[1] On Wright see E. G. R. Taylor, *Mathematical Practitioners of Tudor and Stuart England* (Cambridge, 1954), pp. 45–46, 48, 181.

[2] City Records, Journals 25, f. 180b. There is a reference in H.M.C. *Cecil MSS.* xii. 370 to the question whether Cecil wanted Wright's water brought to his new house in the Strand, which seems a long way from Leadenhall.

Council to give instructions to the J.P.s for Hertfordshire and Middlesex to do all in their power to assist him and his men.[1] The Privy Council evidently complied with this request, for on 20 July the account book records the payment of a fee of £2 'to Mr. Corbet, Clearke of the Counsell, for the Lords l[ett]res to the Justices of Peace and for thear open plackard in my behalf to all officers'. Steps were also taken, in accordance with the procedure laid down in the act of 1606, for settling the compensation to landowners, for on 2 August £2. 10s. was paid 'for a Comyssion owt of the Chaunsserye to Compounde with men for ther lande'.

For a few months good progress was made. At the end of August the names of over fifty labourers appear in the accounts, and a month later the number had risen to over 130.[2] During the autumn the number varied, possibly according to the weather, but in several weeks it was over 100, and it never fell below 47. In the new year, however, it becomes clear that something was wrong, and for the week ending 27 January 1610 only 17 labourers received wages. Wright's allowance ceased after 10 February, and then for twenty-two months work was virtually at a standstill. Colthurst's name, as we have seen, disappears from the accounts in June, and there were periods when the only items recorded were the weekly wages of the clerk (12s.) and the molecatcher (3s. 4d.), whose services no doubt were required to safeguard the work already completed.[3] For the same purpose the first four of the walksmen, whose business it still is to patrol the river, were appointed about this time, and were paid their first quarter's wages at midsummer 1610. Between them they only received £1, and no doubt Mr. Berry is right in assuming that their duties were only part-time.[4]

---

[1] W. H. and H. C. Overall, *Analytical Index to . . . Remembrancia* (1878), p. 555.

[2] Not all full-time, however. Some were paid for six days' work, some for five, four, or less. One death is recorded: on 26 Dec. 1609 2s. was paid 'for the buriall of Tho. Trenson the Scottishman'.

[3] Occasionally the 'moule taker' did 'over worke' (i.e. overtime) and was paid 5s.

[4] *Proc. Soc. Cymmrodorion* 1956 (1957), p. 25. By Michaelmas the number was reduced to two, paid 10s., and then for the ensuing year there were three, paid £1 a quarter. At Michaelmas 1611 there were again two, the third (John Allen) being employed 'for keeping the springe heade' as well as 'lookeing to the river'.

It is clear that the reason for the stoppage was not that any special physical or engineering difficulty had been encountered. Opposition was entirely human, and seems to have originated with a few landowners who obstinately refused to agree to the river being taken through their estates. For the first ten miles, it seems, the landowners had been friendly and co-operative, and 'of their good likinge to the worke' some had actually given their land without demanding compensation. But a certain 'Mr. Auditour Purvey', though apparently 'well satisfied for a while', later 'for reasons best knowen to himselfe began all theis mischeafes out of mallice and splenie'. Two others had then joined him in refusing a settlement, and they organized a formidable campaign against Myddelton and his work.[1] The city meanwhile did its best on Myddelton's behalf. On 17 April the Remembrancer was instructed to draft a letter to the Privy Council in the name of the Lord Mayor and aldermen, asking them 'to be mediators to the King's most excellent Majesty that all letts and hindrances may be removed and way given to Mr. Midleton to proceede in the bringinge of the Ryver of water from Amwell and Chawdwell to the north parts of the cittie'.[2] The opposition, however, took their case to Parliament, and by May of 1610 there seemed every prospect of their gaining the support of their fellow landowners in the House of Commons for a Bill to repeal the Acts that authorized the making of the river. On 9 May Mr. Beaulieu wrote a letter to a friend named Trumbull, who lived at Brussels, in which, after mentioning the debates about wardships and the Great Contract, he went on to refer to 'much ado . . . in the House about the work undertaken and far advanced already by Middleton, of the cutting of a River and bringing it to London . . . through the Grounds of many Men, who for their particular interests do strongly oppose themselves to it, and are like (as 'tis said) to overthrow it all'.[3]

The Bill to repeal 'the acts for the river from Ware' received its first reading in the Commons on 18 May 1610;[4] a week later

<hr />

[1] Bodl. Tanner MS. 98, f. 113. On Purvey see below, p. 47.

[2] City Records, Repertories 29, f. 206.

[3] R. Winwood, *Memorials of Affairs of State in the Reigns of Queen Elizabeth and King James I* (1725), iii. 160.   [4] *C.J.* i. 429.

the city authorities sent a deputation, consisting of two aldermen, the Town Clerk, and the Remembrancer, to wait upon Sir John Herbert, one of the Secretaries of State, Sir Julius Caesar, Chancellor of the Exchequer, and Sir Thomas Parry, Chancellor of the Duchy (all of whom were at the same time Privy Councillors and M.P.s), and also upon 'such others of the parliament house as they are acquainted withall'. The deputation were instructed 'in the name of the cittie earnestlie to move and intreate their lawfull favours for the hindring' of the Bill then before Parliament, on the ground that the supply of fresh water would be beneficial to health, and that the stream had 'already been brought onwards about tenn miles, at the charges of Mr. Hugh Midleton the cittie's deputy amounting already to the some of three thowsand pounds and above'.[1] In spite of this the Bill was read a second time and committed on 20 June, and when ten days later a petition was sent in from 'gentlemen of the country', alleging damage to their property, ten members of the Commons committee were appointed on 16 July to 'view the river'; but as the session was nearing its close, the Bill was held over till the next session.[2]

The arguments used in the campaign against the New River, and the answers marshalled in its favour by Myddelton and his supporters, can be gathered from a document among the State Papers in the Public Record Office, in which the 'Obiections against the river' and 'Answeares to the same obiections' are set out in parallel columns.[3] There is another copy of this document among the Tanner Manuscripts in the Bodleian Library,[4] and on both is inscribed in Myddelton's own bold handwriting, but with slight variations in spelling, the statement: 'This bill preferred is to repeale the twooe Acts made in the 3 and 4th yeare of his Majesty's reign, upon which Actes there is about 3000li. laid out and the water brought about tenn myles.' The copy in the Bodleian is accompanied by two other papers, evidently part of the propaganda put out by the opposing forces, headed

---

[1] Repertories 29, f. 231; R. R. Sharpe, *London and the Kingdom*, ii. 22. The figure £3,000 was an exaggeration, more than double the expenditure later certified (see below, p. 48).

[2] *C.J.* i. 442, 444, 450.   [3] S.P.D. James I, 78, no. 106.

[4] Bodl. Tanner MS. 98, f. 49.

respectively 'Bennefitts that by this river may growe to the cittie of London and generally to all England being good water for all purposes',[1] and 'Obiections or maledicōns against the newe ryver with answere'.[2]

The objections stated in this paper, and the answers set out after each, though in a different order, are substantially the same as those in the paper bearing Myddelton's endorsement. They fall under two main headings: (1) objections to taking the water from the springs, which otherwise would flow into the Lea; (2) objections to the course of the New River itself. Under the first heading it was alleged that diverting the springs would lower the level of the Lea and so hinder navigation 'with vessels of great burthen', to which the reply was that official inquiries had shown that the Lea was not affected, and in any case the only navigation on the Lea was by barges. Another objection was that mills on the Lea would suffer, to which it was replied that there was more than enough water for the mills, and if any were injured the statute provided for compensation. An allegation that meadows adjacent to the Lea, 'whereby they are nourished', would 'decay', was also summarily dismissed.

There were twelve objections under the second heading, some of which may represent genuine apprehensions, but others were fairly obviously trumped up for the occasion. It was alleged, for example, that the New River would be 'a perpetuall cause of quarrells amongst them, being barred from their old waies and soe enforced to trespasse one another'. This was clearly nonsense, and the reply pointed out that there were 'convenient bridges in all the old waies'. Another objection was that the river would alter the soil for the worse, turning 'meadowes into bogges and quagmires and errable [arable] into squallie grounds', but this too was dismissed, experience showing that on the contrary 'the soyle adjoyning is the better and not the worse for the river'. Another objection was 'the mangling of their lande lying in comon fields into quilletts and small peeces'. This sounds a more

---

[1] Bodl. Tanner MS. 98, f. 47.

[2] Ibid., f. 48. A third paper (f. 113, already referred to above, p. 29, n. 4) gives a brief history of the undertaking from the time of Colthurst's original proposal to Queen Elizabeth.

serious inconvenience, and all Myddelton's supporters could offer in reply was that in such cases compensation would be paid. In the other paper they had to admit that some such cutting up of individual properties was unavoidable, since 'of necessitie Levell must be observed', but they said that to mitigate this 'consideracōn' should be exercised. Another objection, concerning damage 'upon soden raynes by inondacōnes', was answered by reference to arrangements for land water to pass either over or under the river, while if the river itself rose above a certain height there were hatches through which the surplus water would be drawn off.[1] Apprehensions were also expressed that cornfields would be damaged owing to 'the libertie which the cittie hath with men, horses, carts and carriages to repaire the banckes of the same cutt from tyme to tyme', and that at least as much land on either side of the river would be spoilt 'by throwing up the earth on both sides' as was taken up by the watercourse itself. Compensation was the answer to these objections, and fears that the highway between Ware and London would be 'annoyed and like to be made impassable' were dismissed as groundless, as was the allegation that 'the cutt is noe better than a verie deepe ditch and dangerous pitt for drowning of men and cattell'. It was admitted that the cut had to be made deep in one or two places, but the danger was denied. The promoters were perhaps over sanguine in this regard, for on 9 January 1622 the King himself, when out riding in Theobalds Park, was thrown from his horse and fell head first into the river, which at the time was slightly frozen over, so that only his boots appeared above the surface. He was pulled out by Sir Richard Young, and 'there came much water out of his mouth and body', but he was able to ride back to Theobalds, got into a warm bed, and was none the worse for the experience.[2]

Another objection, put forward by Dr. Atkins, who owned property in Cheshunt parish, was that the church would suffer from a diminution of tithes, but this was dismissed as a trifle:

[1] When just before Christmas 1614 there was flooding near Cheshunt £16. 14s. 4d. was paid out as compensation.

[2] J. Nichols, *The Progresses, Processions and Magnificent Festivities of King James the First* (1828), iv. 749.

the mile of river in his parish took less than an acre of land, 'the tithe whereof is not worth above ijs. vjd. a yere'. Lastly the objectors grumbled because the city had done nothing to bring the water to London, but had 'granted their whole interest in fee simple to Mr. Middleton and his heires, who doth the same for his private benefitt'. The answer to this was that 'if the maior and cittizens would not adventure upon so uncertaine a worke, Mr. Middleton deserveth the greater cōmendacōn in adventuringe his monie and travell for the good of the cittie, and if the cittie finde good and the countrie no hurt, though Mr. Middleton gayneth by it, he deserveth it well'.

Besides answering these objections, Myddelton's supporters composed a statement of the positive benefits to be expected from the river. They stressed the advantage of getting water '25 foote high in any house in London or within the liberties or suburbes', so that 'pore people' would no longer be 'inforced to use foule and unwholesome water which breedeth great infections'. At night surplus water would 'runne into the towne ditches and so to the tower ditche and at pleasure to the fleete ditch and common sewers', while 'in extremitie of heate' it would be possible 'to lett runne the cocks to coole the streets and clenze the kennells, whereby to avoide all ill aires and infeccōns'. Water would also 'be in a redines for danger of fires'. Nor would Londoners be the only gainers. Apart from the employment its construction gave to '1700 poore men', once the river was past Cheshunt it would be 'welcome to all the reste of the country', for in dry summers most people living between there and London had to drive their cattle two or three miles to water. Indeed, many occupiers of land on the section of river already completed were so well satisfied that they would give 'larg somes of money rather than the water shall goe backe againe'.

The new session opened on 16 October 1610, but no more was heard of the repealing Bill, or of the committee appointed to 'view the river'. At length, on 29 November, in an effort to get things moving again, the city sent a humble petition to the Commons, begging them 'to appoint some such as they shall thinke fitt to veiw the said worke and reporte what they conceive thereof to the intent that unles the sugestions prove true (as the peticioners assuredly beleave they will not) a worke of so publique use having allready receaved a probacōn of two sessions of parliament may be no longer hindred by causelesse opposicōn'.[1] The Commons, however, had other business in hand, and nothing had been done when in February 1611 the King dissolved Parliament. It has sometimes been assumed that Myddelton was thus set free to proceed,[2] but though his opponents had, at any rate for the time being, failed to secure the repeal of his statutory powers, and he did in fact finish the river before the next Parliament met in 1614, at the moment the outlook was far from clear, and, as it turned out, months were still to elapse before he could resume operations. Myddelton therefore asked the city to allow him more time to complete the work; the Common Council, 'finding no delaie to bee in him', consented, and granted him an extension of five years.[3] On 28 March 1611 he entered into a new agreement with the city, and the previous agreement was cancelled.

Myddelton may have found fresh cause for uneasiness in what looked like another competitive scheme for supplying London with water from the Lea. The King had recently founded a College of Divinity at Chelsea,[4] and its Provost and Fellows, short of funds and led to believe that they might supplement them 'by imitating Morice and forestalling Myddelton', obtained an Act of Parliament 'for bringing fresh streams of water by engine from Hackney Marsh to the City of London, for the benefit of Chelsea Hospital'.[5] Though this extraordinary threat apparently never materialized, there was another potential competitor in Edward Hayes, who sought Lord Salisbury's support for some waterworks which he claimed were 'better than the Amwell waters', though he added that the city needed Myddelton's supply as well as his.[6] Apart from competitors, opposition to Myddelton

[1] City Records: Letter Book DD, f. 223.
[2] Thus S. R. Gardiner in *History of England*, ii. 215.
[3] Journals 28, f. 176 verso.
[4] Cf. R. Winwood, *Memorials*, iii. 160.
[5] 7 James I, c. 9. See F. Clifford, *History of Private Bill Legislation*, ii. 67; Selden Soc., vol. 28 (1913), p. cxxiv.
[6] *Cal. S.P.D. 1611–18*, p. 78.

was still active, and in August 1611 further objections were voiced against the city having handed over their statutory powers, 'by which means that which was intended for a public good shall be converted into a private gain'. Among other objections complaint was made that Myddelton intended 'to bring this water to a pond in a field between Islington and Clerkenwell . . . and so to convey it by pipes into divers places . . . where he may vent it most to his profit, whereas by the statute the whole stream is to be brought to the north parts of London, which the city engaged to do by bringing it to Moorfields to keep the city sweet'.[1]

Faced with these uncertainties and difficulties, it may well have seemed to Myddelton that the best hope of progress lay in getting the King himself on his side. It has often been assumed that James first became interested in the river when he saw the channel for it being dug in his park at Theobalds, near Enfield, but it is clear that it had not been taken nearly as far as this when work was suspended. In fact the stoppage seems to have occurred at Wormley, where the river made the first of its big loops, and this may indeed be what gave rise to the objections to it. It is probable that as negotiations proceeded Myddelton met the King, but discussions were first opened with the Lord Treasurer, Lord Salisbury, with whom Myddelton had previously been in touch when settling the compensation payable for passage through his property in the Ryefield at Hoddesdon.[2] Various reasons have been suggested for the King's participation in the venture. It has generally been assumed that the initiative was Myddelton's, and that his object was financial help. On the other hand it has been suggested that the impecunious King saw in Myddelton's troubles an opportunity to become a partner in what he hoped would be a profitable undertaking. This seems to be the view of Thomas Fuller, who after praising Myddelton and his labours, 'encountering all the way with an army of oppositions, grappling with hills, struggling with rocks, fighting with forests', remarks: 'But, oh what an injury was it unto him, that a potent Person and idle Spectator should strike in; (Reader, I could heartily wish it

---

[1] *Rep. H.M.C.* iii (1872), App., p. 58 (Duke of Northumberland's MSS.).
[2] M.W.B. Compensation Receipt.

were a falsehood what I report) and by his greatness possess a
moiety of the profit, which the unwearied endeavours of the
foresaid knight had purchased to himself!'[1]

In fact, the benefits expected were probably mutual. If the
King hoped for profit he was to be disappointed, but for all his
faults he was genuinely interested in 'improvements', and as
Gardiner remarked (apparently intending as much blame as
praise), he 'seldom turned a deaf ear to any scheme which tended
to the material welfare of his subjects'.[2] No doubt from Myddelton's
point of view the King's financial help was welcome, but perhaps
the most important advantage was that with the King behind
him Myddelton could overcome the opposition of recalcitrant
landowners like Mr. Purvey of Wormley and his friends. There
is even a possibility that the King may have privately engineered
the opposition, so that Myddelton might be driven to enlist his
support. At any rate it may be significant that two of the principal
objectors were royal servants. William Purvey, as his magnificent
monument in Wormley church proclaims, was 'one of his Maties
Auditors of the Duchy of Lancaster . . . , who lived in the grace
and favour of his Prince'; Henry Atkins's more modest monument in Cheshunt church shows that he was Doctor of Physic
and 'Physician in Ordinary for the space of 32 yeares to King
James and King Charles'.

However that may be, negotiations between Salisbury and
Myddelton continued during the summer of 1611. Salisbury on
behalf of the King promised assistance in removing 'unjust and
unlawful impediments', and in procuring the issue of 'com-
myssions under the greate Seale of England for laying out of
convenyent lymitts of grounde for the making of the trench of
the said Ryver'. Myddelton 'with his workmen carts cariages and
other necessaryes' was to be allowed to enter the King's lands
'and there to digg cutt and caste upp the soyle thereof as should
be fytt and necessarye for the effectinge and performance of the
same worke and that without compoundinge or payeinge anye
thinge therefore to his highnes his heires or successors'. The

[1] T. Fuller, *The Worthies of England* (ed. J. Nichols), ii. 590.
[2] S. R. Gardiner, *Hist. Eng.* ii. 215.

financial basis of the agreement was that, in return for half the profits, the King would contribute half the expenditure, past as well as future, and as a warrant for this Myddelton was to produce before Sir Julius Caesar, the Chancellor of the Exchequer, a sworn declaration of his expenses hitherto, and accounts were to be kept in which all future disbursements were to be entered and certified on behalf of both sides. These arrangements were embodied in an agreement between the Lord Treasurer and Myddelton, dated 5 November 1611; six months later, on 2 May 1612, the transaction was completed by a formal indenture between James I and 'Hugh Midleton, citizen and goldsmyth of London', the terms of which were based substantially on the previous agreement with Lord Salisbury.[1] Two other clauses in the indenture are worth noticing. One provided for the suppression of 'tumultuous or other undue or unlawfull courses' in 'hindrance lett or opposition' to the work. The other was a characteristic example of Myddelton's generosity to the poor: the King, it said, was 'pleased and contented that the said Hugh Midleton shoulde and mighte at his owne charges derive a quill out of the mayne pype ... to serve the poore people gratis about St. John's Streete and Westgate Streete which are not able nor fitt to paye for theire water and the same are to be enioyed by the said poore perpetuallye'.

It was in accordance with this agreement that the account books already mentioned as the source of much of our knowledge of the making of the river were kept. Myddelton, of course, had kept a record of his expenses from the beginning of the enterprise, and these occupy the whole of the first book, which ends on 24 August 1611. The first four pages, recording expenses up to 11 August 1609, are in Myddelton's own unmistakable bold handwriting; thereafter the accounts were kept weekly by his clerk, Edward Hughes, but Myddelton signed every page, and himself entered at the foot the total of that page, the total carried forward, and at the head of each page the total brought forward from previous pages. At the end of the book appears Sir Julius Caesar's signature, certifying that the total entered in the book, £1,139. 15s. 11d.,

[1] Close Roll 10 James I (P.R.O., C. 54/2115); *Cal. S.P.D. 1611–18*, p. 128.

had been sworn to by Myddelton. The other eight books, which were signed by Myddelton and Miles Whitacres (later replaced by Edward Ball), whom Salisbury appointed to represent the King's interest, were all kept by William Lewyn,[1] who succeeded Hughes as Myddelton's clerk when Hughes became ill.[2] Hughes's identity is uncertain, but he may have been a descendant of the Edward Hughes who was Receiver-General to Queen Elizabeth of the revenues of North Wales and Cheshire. He came from Holt Castle in Denbighshire, and was thus a Welsh neighbour of Myddelton, who always showed a marked inclination to give employment to his fellow-countrymen.[3] The second clerk, William Lewyn, seems to have been a younger brother of Sir Justinian Lewyn (1586–1620), a gentleman of the Privy Chamber to James I,[4] and his appointment, coming at a time when Myddelton was negotiating with the King, may indicate court influence, or a desire to stand well with the court.

With the conclusion of the agreement with Salisbury, work on the river was resumed, and from the end of November it went ahead rapidly. As a kind of thank-offering for the renewal of work, £15. 7s. was distributed on 4 January 1612 'for gratueties given as a token of the newe yeere, tooe such as have geven greate furtherance tooe the workes, and have taken greate paynes and have done manye kyndenes theirein'. The first sign in the accounts that the stoppage was coming to an end (apart from the resumption of Colthurst's allowance) was the payment of £1 on 28 September 1611 'Tooe Mr. Wrighte when hee came tooe trye the Leavell in Chesthunte parke'; and in October William Parnell,

---

[1] But the totals of each page, and running totals up to date, carried forward to the top of each page, are still in Myddelton's own hand, up to the end of the seventh book. The eighth and ninth books (L.R. 2/32 and 33) were attested by Rowland Backhouse, William Bateman, or Richard Myddelton.

[2] One of the first items in the second book is 16s. 7d. paid on 1 Sept. 1611 'for Mr. Midleton's charges at Hodsedonne three dayes, when Mr. Hughes the Clarke was sicke, beinge with hym to take his accomptes'.

[3] On Hughes see H. A. Shield, 'Links with Shakespeare', in 195 N. & Q. (1950), pp. 206, 385–6.

[4] See Sir Gyles Isham, 'Family Connections of Bp. Brian Duppa', in 196 N. & Q. (1951), pp. 508–9. William Lewyn's son was another Sir Justinian (1613–73), Master in Chancery, who is referred to in the New River Company's charred minutes as being concerned in 1637 in negotiations on the occasion of a dispute between William Lewyn and the company.

who supplied timber for the works, received an advance of £60 for bridges over the river.[1] Wright's name does not appear again in the accounts, and his place as Myddelton's 'arts man' was taken by Edward Pond. Wright died in 1615, but it does not seem that ill health was the reason for the termination of his employment. According to a statement in the annals of Gonville and Caius College, Cambridge, he was 'the first undertaker of that difficult but useful work, by which a little river is brought from Ware in a new Canal, to supply the city of London with water, but by the tricks of others he was hindered from compleating the work he had begun'.[2] This is confirmed by some remarks of the Rev. Wilhelm Bedwell, vicar of Tottenham. After saying that the New River was 'brought with an ill will from Ware to London', which may refer to the hostility of some of the landowners, but possibly to resentment aroused by the dismissal of Wright, he goes on to recall that 'hee who first chalked out the way ... was ... our English Tycho,[3] a man so ingenious, industrious, and learned, that I suppose there were few things undertaken by him, if fecible, which hee would not have done'. Yet 'before the worke was altogether finished, he was put by it, and others imployed to make an end of it'.[4] There may have been some disagreement between Myddelton and Wright, though Myddelton was not the kind of man to treat his helpers badly.

Pond, who was a physician and teacher of mathematics, and is best known as the compiler of popular almanacs, makes his first appearance in the accounts on 30 November 1611, when £1. 17s. 6d. is entered 'For Mr. Midleton's charges at Hodsedonne when hee came downe with Mr. Ponde and Mr. Blagrave toe take the plott betweene Chesthunte and Theoballes'. John Blagrave, who was also an eminent mathematician, had specialized in the construction of astronomical and surveying instruments, and he was evidently a close friend of Pond's, for on his death-bed he

[1] A page at the end of the first account book records the number of planks, bridges, and other timber works supplied by Parnell.

[2] C. Hutton, *Mathematical Tables* (1785), p. 28 n.

[3] The reference is to the famous Danish astronomer Tycho Brahe (1546–1601).

[4] W. Bedwell, *A Briefe Description of the towne of Tottenham Highcrosse ... in the County of Middlesex* (1631), I. viii.

sent for Pond, and entrusted him with his papers and instruments.[1] Blagrave lived at Swallowfield, near Reading, where he had as neighbours Samuel Backhouse, owner of the site of the New River Head at Clerkenwell, and one of the original Adventurers in the New River, and his son John Backhouse, also an Adventurer, and it may well have been they who introduced Blagrave and Pond to Myddelton and got him to engage them.[2] Blagrave, who probably died in 1612, is not mentioned in the accounts after 7 December 1611, but Pond remained in Myddelton's employment, marking out the course for the river, until shortly after the opening ceremony at New River Head at Michaelmas 1613. He was paid weekly £2. 6s. 8d. 'for his weekes entertainment', and he owned a level, presumably some kind of instrument on a stand, for in the middle of February 1612 'Davie Gryffethe the Trumpeter' and 'Rees Uphughes' were paid 12s. 'for carrieing the Leavell 6 dayes a peece att 12d. per diem'. On 8 April 5s. 4d. was spent 'for 4 Ells of Canvas att xvjd. the elle for to make a Shelter for Mr. Ponde's leavell'. Pond was well aware of the value of his services, for, years after the completion of the river, he inserted it in his almanac in the list of important events in the history of the world. Thus, in the almanac for 1627 we read:[3]

> Since the river from Ware to Lond begun by me Ed Pond 15 [years]
> Since it was finished by me (the sole Artist) Ed Pond 14

All the same, he had some reason for pride in his achievement, for in the whole course of the river from Chadwell, as originally made about 40 miles long, the total fall is only about 18 feet, or just over 5 inches in a mile. Actually the river was held up by sluices at several points, and between the sluices the fall was even less than this, between 2 and 3 inches a mile, which must

---

[1] See E. G. R. Taylor, *Mathematical Practitioners*, pp. 181, 198. Pond refers to Blagrave's dying gift in his Almanac for 1612.

[2] I owe this to a typewritten note kindly given me by Mr. G. C. Berry, in correction of the account in his lecture (*Trans. Soc. Cymmr.* 1956 (1957), pp. 30, 31). The *D.N.B.* gives the date of Blagrave's death as 9 Aug. 1611, but this seems to be an error for 1612.

[3] A corresponding item does not appear in the 1626 Almanac, but Pond included it for years afterwards. Aubrey records its insertion in the Almanac for 1647 (note in A. Clark's edn. of *Brief Lives*, ii. 1).

have demanded great accuracy in surveying. In effect the river closely followed the 100-foot contour line, with numerous loops to the westward as it traversed the valleys of successive tributaries of the Lea. The Round Pond at Clerkenwell, where the river was to end, was well sited, for it stood about 80 feet above sea-level, on the nearest piece of high ground overlooking the city from the north.

Once work was resumed, progress was fairly rapid, and the thirty odd miles of river between Wormley and Islington were completed in under two years. The occurrence of place-names in the accounts enables the advance to be traced in detail. During the early months of 1612 the trench was being dug through Cheshunt; in April and May, at Theobalds and Enfield; in June at Edmonton; by July the workmen had reached Southgate and Wood Green. After that there was a pause of some months, no doubt to consolidate and complete the work done so far. The left-hand side, where the ground sloped away, often caused trouble, and the bank had to be raised or remade, or strengthened with clay and piles, or the trench had to be deepened; sometimes, when an error had been made, it had to be filled in and another cut dug. Occasionally, too, there were fresh human as well as physical difficulties. In August 1613, over a year after the trench had been cut through Theobalds Park, the King gave orders that banks should be erected, costing £30, to prevent the river from flooding Bromley Grove, and this was not the only occasion when he interfered with the work. In November of the same year £5. 4s. was spent on 'altering the Cutt in John Gyrton's Parke which his Matie founde faulte withall'. Entries in the accounts, and receipts preserved at the offices of the Metropolitan Water Board, show that compensation was paid to most of the owners of land on the course of the river,[1] but there were a few who for 'the great love they bore to the city of London' allowed it to be taken through their property free of charge. Notable among

---

[1] Sometimes they stood out for exorbitant amounts, and settlement of their claims took a long time. On the back of the receipt (M.W.B., no. 123) from a man named Nicholson, who originally demanded £9. 14s. 6d., Myddelton wrote the following order: 'Mr. Lewyn I praie you paie Mr. Nicholes the 3 li. 6/8d. and take his acquittance upon this arbattrament 30th June 1615. Hugh Myddelton.'

these was the vicar of Amwell, the Rev. Thomas Hassall, and in return Myddelton spent £2. 7s. 'for a greate Churche Bible geven toe the parish of Amwell in good speede of the Water to the Cittie of London'. He also gave money for the poor of the parish (e.g. £2 on 4 December 1613 'in respecte of their Losse and hyndrance ... by reason of the Leakeadge of the Ryver through the Bankes'), and left them a legacy of £5 in his will. Mr. Hassall assisted Myddelton on several occasions and advanced money towards the expenses of the river. A page at the end of the first account book records the receipt of 20s. from him on 9 August 1609, and another 40s. two days later. In the autumn of 1609 several more substantial advances, of £5 or £6, were received from 'my mistress Thorogood' of Hoddesdon, and similar sums came from her weekly in March and April 1610, and at intervals until July 1611. These sums were probably short-term loans. Considering the difficulty of carrying money in those days, it must have been a great convenience for Myddelton that some people were willing to act as bankers for him at that distance from town.[1]

The accounts give many details of the methods of construction as well as of materials used, workmen employed, and wages paid. 'A Dosen & a halfe of Basketts toe carrie earthe uppon the Bancke' cost 5s. 6d.; 'xij hoddes to carrie earth where the wheele Barrowes cannot goe' cost 18s. 'Tooe Beetles toe dryve pyles' were bought for 1s. 6d., 'an Iron Crowe to make way for the piles in pynninge of the heads' for 4s. On 25 November 1609 John Rogers was paid £2. 17s. for 4,000 bricks, and on the same day he also received 16s. 8d. 'for xl^{tie} bushells of lime at vd. the bushell'. The work of excavation and making up the banks was carried out by gangs of labourers, but in the early days, before the stoppage at Wormley, a mechanical contrivance called 'the Ingen' was used. John Aubrey records that 'a Country Fellow seeing them digging the Channel for the new River said that he would save them 2000 pounds, that is, he would turn up the Earth with a Plough; and had strong Ploughs and Harness made purposely, which was drawn by 17 Horses, and sav'd a vast deal

---

[1] I owe this suggestion to Mr. G. C. Berry.

of Expence'.[1] A number of entries in the accounts refer to the use of this machine in October and November 1609:

> Mr. Hellam for xiij horses and his men two daies to drawe the Ingen, £2. 3s. 4d.
> For the rudder post, for the yoke and timber used about the Ingen, 4s. 4d.
> For tallow for the Ingen & cart, 8d.
> To Essex for bread & drinke for the Carters when the Ingen wente, 8d.
> To Harvey & Saringe for watching the waights in the Ingen, 8d.
> To Lupton for his cattel for to draw the Ingen, 8s. 0d.

Sometimes repairs were needed:

> For a board for the Ingen, 8d.
> A new shaft for the Ingen, 2s. 4d.
> To a Carpenter for worke aboute the Ingen, 1s. 4d.
> For thre traces for the Ingen 2s. 6d.
> To Tho. Bateman the wheles and Jo. Damper the smithe for worke for the Ingen, £9. 11s. 8d.

In September 1609, before the Ingen is specifically mentioned, the accounts contain a number of items for repairs to 'the plough', which may perhaps refer to the same machine. It looks, however, as if the Ingen did not prove particularly efficient, or it may have broken down, for when work was suspended in 1610 it was taken to Mr. Thorogood's at Hoddesdon, and did not reappear.

The most elaborate construction on the river was the Bush Hill Frame, near Edmonton. The valley of the Salmon Brook is comparatively narrow, and the river was taken across on a wooden aqueduct instead of making the long detour which would have been necessary if it had followed a level course around the head of the valley. The frame was an open trough, 660 feet long, about 6 feet wide and 5 feet deep, and was originally supported on 'arches of wood fixed in the ground, some whereof are four and twentie foote in heighth'.[2] Later it was lined with lead, and the timber arches were replaced by an embankment, on which stood eighty brick piers supporting the timber uprights, but originally

---

[1] J. Aubrey, *Brief Lives* (ed. O. L. Dick, 1949), p. 198. This passage does not occur in Clark's edition of Aubrey.

[2] E. Howes, *Continuation of John Stow's Annales or a Generall Chronicle of England* (1631), p. 1015.

View of the New River, as conveyed through the Frame at Bush Hill

the whole structure was made of wood, and caulked. The construction of it was entrusted to Parnell, the timber supplier, and no details appear in the accounts, but by January 1614 it needed extensive repairs, and the materials required for this purpose, and the prices paid for them, are all recorded.[1] Four or five years later a similar but rather shorter frame was built at Highbury to cross the Hackney Brook, and so cut out a loop of the river, which originally extended as far west as the Holloway Road. This frame, which became known as the Boarded River, was erected in August and September 1619 along the top of an artificial embankment which had taken between eight and nine months to complete, and like the Bush Hill Frame it was made entirely of wood. These structures were objects of wondering admiration to contemporaries, but they needed frequent repairs and always leaked. They survived until the second half of the eighteenth century, and were then replaced by raising the embankments.[2]

When the river on a contour-line course had to cross a stream, an embankment on a smaller scale was thrown up, and the stream was taken underneath the river in a culvert. Sometimes, however (e.g. at Wormley, Enfield, and elsewhere), the stream was banked up and carried over the river in a wooden trough called a flash, and, if required, land water, or the water from the stream, could be diverted into the river itself. Besides the flashes, large quantities of timber were used all along the river for wharfing the banks and making bridges. A wooden bridge cost 40s. (thus, on 20 February 1613 £42 was paid 'to Jeffreye Bennett for settinge upp xxj Carte Bridges in Mr. Hawkins severall groundes att xls. a Bridge'), and

---

[1] 400 boards 'to lyne the bottome of the frame to kepe in the Cawkeyn' at 9s. the 100; 3 barrels of 'tarre' at 20s. the barrel; 900 of 'Rossen' at 8s. the 100; 700 of 'pytche' at 10s. the 100; 500 of 'oakeam' at 9s. the 100; 100 lbs. of 'hard tallowe to mingle with' the pitch, tar, and rosin. At the same time a load of tileshards was bought to underpin the frame, and £5. 3s. worth of half-crown nails, two-shilling nails, 'double tennes', 'single tennes', and sixpenny nails. The caulking was done by shipwrights, earning 2s. a day.

[2] The Highbury Frame was the first to go, in 1776. The *Gentleman's Magazine* for Sept. 1784 (vol. liv, p. 643) contains a description and illustration of the Bush Hill Frame, then shortly to be demolished. Facing p. 723 is a perspective view of an imposing brick arch, still existing, under the Bush Hill embankment, bearing Myddelton's arms above the keystone. It was rebuilt in 1682. See also ibid., p. 803. During the Gordon Riots in 1780 there was a threat to destroy the Bush Hill Frame, and a party of cavalry was stationed there for some days to guard it (W. Robinson, *History and Antiquities of the Parish of Edmonton* (1819), p. 18 n.).

the carpenters, of whom large numbers were employed, generally earned 1*s*. 4*d*. a day. There were also brick bridges in places, which cost rather more: £7. 3*s*. 6*d*. was paid 'to Steeven Boone for makeinge a great Brick Bridge at Islingtowne towne end, being 18 foote wyde'. Bricklayers earned 1*s*. 6*d*. a day. On 9 May 1612 Thomas Springfeild and Robert Nottingham were paid £40 'toe make provision of Brick & lyme for bridges and other necessarie uses for the Ryver, for wch theye have entred into bondes to his Mātie, for the makeinge of soe manye bridges or other works as shall amounte to the some of fortie poundes'. When they had fulfilled their contract their work was inspected, and on 7 November 1612 5*s*. was paid 'toe Mr. Browne a Master Worke man of London for his paynes toe come and veiwe the Bryck Brydges wch Springfeild & Nottingham made'. Later (February 1613) a more thorough inspection took place: 'To Mr. Burgen for his paynes & charges toe surveye all the workes & for his Directions for the furtheraunce of the worke', £4.

In some weeks over 200 general labourers were employed, earning 10*d*. a day, but the work of excavating was paid at piece rates, varying with the depth and the nature of the soil. Average rates ranged from 4*d*. a pole or rod at 6-inch depth, and 10*d*. at 1-foot depth, to 9*s*. 6*d*. at 10 foot, and 12*s*. at 13 foot. For a short period in 1609 and again in 1612 the rate of pay was expressed in 'gauges', 'single gauge' being paid at 1*s*. 2*d*. a rod, and other depths proportionately more. Thus £1. 5*s*. 10*d*. was paid 'to Henry Stanly and his companie for 11 pole ¾ by them fully done at double gage'; 'more to them for xiij pole single gaged' 15*s*. 2*d*.; 'To John Dolyn and his companie for 7½ pole at treble gage 3*s*. 6*d*. a pole', £1. 2*s*. 6*d*. The size of the gauges is not specified, but the payments made suggest that single gauge indicated a depth of about 18 inches, double gauge about 3 feet, and treble gauge about 6 feet. Sometimes, but not always, an extra 2*d*. a day was earned for work in the water; thus Jo: Gilderson and Henry Denton earned 12*s*. 'for 6 daies in the water'. Dirty work was sometimes recognized by extra pay, but if bad weather prevented work pay was stopped: on one occasion 131 labourers were paid for work '5 dayes a peece, but all the 2*d*. was abated by reason a peece of one afternoone proved fowle'. The men were summoned to work by a drum, purchased on 21 March 1612 at a cost of 14s.

Trees often stood in the way of the river and had to be felled or uprooted. In the early days (16 December 1609) near Broxbourne church a tree was pulled down at a cost of only 3d. to the sexton for borrowing his ropes, but usually the removal of trees cost about a shilling each. A 'great oak' cost 2s. to uproot; three great oaks were felled for 3s. 6d. Apart from the original construction, many items in the accounts are concerned with maintenance and repairs. Sometimes the banks caved in and the resulting mound of earth in the middle of the stream had to be removed; this was called 'casteing upp a Calfe'. Moles were often responsible for undermining or damaging the banks, and apart from the molecatcher's wages the trouble they caused can be inferred from the numerous entries in the accounts for the purchase of 'molle traps'. Another regular task was cutting weeds in the river. Various materials were used to strengthen or fill in the banks: in one place 6s. was spent 'for Lyme toe putt in the Crackes of the Newe Banck', and we even find 3s. 8d. 'for xi loades of horse dung at Amwell to mende the Bancke at 4d. the load'. On a number of occasions materials had to be supplied for roadmaintenance; for example, on 23 November 1611 3s. 4d. was spent 'for 10 loade of stones for the highe waye at Broxborne streete'. This evidently was not enough, and a week later another twenty loads had to be put down. In July 1612 and again in March 1614 loads of chalk were required to raise the highway at Ware above the level of the river.

In March 1613 the excavation of the channel, which had been suspended since the previous July, was resumed, and the end was soon in sight. Hornsey, Newington, and Holloway were passed during that month, and finally the Mantells[1] at Clerkenwell, where the Round Pond, later called New River Head, was to be made, was reached on 10 April 1613. There was still much consolidation

[1] Apparently a corruption of the name of Geoffrey de Mandeville, to whom the land formerly belonged. It was sometimes called the Commandery Mantells, from having been in the possession of the order of St. John of Jerusalem. See W. J. Pinks, *History of Clerkenwell* (1865), p. 491.

to be done, besides the laying of mains to distribute the watei in the city, and the formal ceremony of inauguration did not take place till the afternoon of Michaelmas Day. Then, to celebrate the completion of the river, a notable pageant was staged, which is described at length by Anthony Munday,[1] who had taken a great and admiring interest in the making of the river, which, as he tells us, he 'did divers times ride to see . . . and diligently observed that admirable Art, Pains and Industry were bestowed for the Passage of it'. It was the day when Hugh Myddelton's elder brother Sir Thomas was elected Lord Mayor for the ensuing year. The assembled company included the Lord Mayor in office, Sir John Swinnerton, Sir Henry Montagu the Recorder, 'and many worthy Aldermen'. Then a troop of some sixty labourers 'well apparelled, and wearing green Monmouth caps',[2] and carrying 'spades, shovels, pickaxes and suchlike instruments of laborious employment', marched, to the accompaniment of drums, two or three times round the cistern, after which one of them recited a metrical speech composed by the dramatist Thomas Middleton.[3] After thirty introductory lines the speaker alluded in turn to some of the leading personalities concerned in the work, beginning with 'the Overseer, this try'd Man, an Ancient Soldier and an Artizan' (Captain Edmund Colthurst). Next came the Clerk (William Lewyn), the Mathematician (Edward Pond), and 'the Master of the Timber-work' (William Parnell). After 'the Measurer, . . . Bricklayer and Engineer' came 'the Borer and the Pavier', who made and laid the elm-trunk pipes in the streets,[4] and lastly, after the labourers, the 'Keeper of Amwell-head' and the Walksmen. The pageant culminated in the opening of the floodgates, and the water flowed into the cistern to the accompaniment of drums and trumpets, and 'a brave Peal of Chambers'.[5]

[1] John Stow's continuator: *Survey of the Cities of London and Westminster* (ed. J. Strype, 1720), i. 26. There is another slightly variant account in J. Nichols, *The Progresses . . . of James I*, ii. 697–701.
[2] Flat round caps formerly worn by soldiers and sailors.
[3] No relation of Sir Hugh's.   [4] See below, p. 61.
[5] i.e. small pieces of ordnance. An imaginary picture of the scene, with the title 'Sir Hugh Middleton's Glory', was engraved by George Bickham in 1772, and dedicated to the New River Company. A copy of it hangs on the staircase at Chirk Castle, the home of Sir Thomas Myddelton's descendant, Lt.-Col. R. Myddelton.

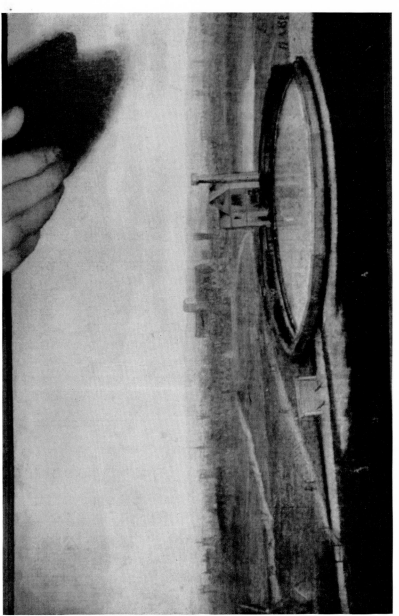

New River Head. Detail from the portrait of Sir John Backhouse in the National Portrait Gallery, London

IV

DISTRIBUTING THE WATER

ON the site of the New River Head at Clerkenwell a pool already stood, 'commonly called the Ducking pond'.[1] This became the Round Pond, and was wharfed with oak boards, of which 4,800 were needed, at 7s. 6d. a hundred. It was surrounded by a brick wall, built by Stephen Boone, whose name appears regularly in the accounts as a contractor for brick bridges, and who also (at a cost of £102. 17s.) built the chimneys and other brickwork in the Water House. This was erected on the south side of the Round Pond, and in the last century it became the headquarters of the undertaking. The materials needed for its construction are recorded in detail in the accounts. 'For Tyles for the house' £7. 14s.; 'for Lyme Sannde Lathes and Nales and for Workemannshipp for tyleinge the howse and for plasteringe the Ceeleing the Couneting howse' £7; 'To Ferdinando Jefford, for Iron Barres and Casements for the Wyndowes of the Cesterne howse, for Lockes and Keyes, hookes, hinges, for spikes, broad nales, other Iron Worke, for the howse as may appere by his Byll and acquittance theireuppon' £27 (all these under date 27 November 1613); 'Toe John Yates for tooe hundrethe and twentye foote of glasse for the Wyndowes about the Cesterne Howse att V^d the foote with tooe shillinges and foure pence over' £4. 14s. (4 December 1613). A few weeks before this (13 November) a carpenter, Richard Sellbye, was paid £1. 6s. for making 'the gallerie within the Cesterne howse, toe stande upon toe turne the stoppcocks'.[2]

---

[1] E. Howes, *Continuation of John Stow's Annales or a Generall Chronicle of England* (1631), pp. 1015b, 1016a. John Backhouse drew £32. 10s. a year as rent 'for the duckinge Ponde and the groundes by itt' (L.R. 2/33).

[2] On the same date Sellbye also received £8 'for Frameing xvj Rodd more for the wharfe within the Pond at xs. per Rodd'. A week before Thomas Russell was paid £34. 10s. 'for xxx Loades of Tymber, for the Wharfe within the Ponde at Islington, being delyvered theireatt xxiijs. per Loade'.

A week later 'hinges and nales for the trappdoore goeing downe into the Cesterne howse' cost 2s. 6d. Water came into the cistern from the Round Pond through a grating, and passed thence into the wooden pipes, made of elm trunks, which carried the water to the city. Later on (5 April 1617) 3s. 4d. was spent 'For oyleinge the Wyer grates that geve ayre into the Cesterne howse att Islington'.

Myddelton was always ready to give employment to his fellow-countrymen, and one of these, 'Howell Joahnes', became custodian of the house at New River Head. 'My man Howell' had appeared quite early in the accounts, but his first regular employment dated from 7 September 1611, when he was engaged as a ganger at 7s. a week (raised to 8s. from 29 February 1612). When the construction of the river was finished he was in charge of the labourers laying mains in the streets; later he had living quarters in the Water House. Together with Boone he was responsible for control of the walksmen who patrolled the river (an entry dated 5 April 1617, which recurs later, records the payment of £87. 10s. 'To Steven Boone and Howell Joahnes for their Quartridge [i.e. a quarter's wages] ended at Lady Daye Laste paste, for meyneteyninge and kepeinge the Ryver, all the waye from Chadwell and Amwell to Islington'). He was paid 100 marks in 1622 for 'his great paynes taken in the workes', and Myddelton continued to think well of him, for he left him £20 in his will. 'Howell Joahnes' remained in the company's employment until his death in 1637, but, latterly at any rate if not before, he must have abused his position, for one of the charred minutes of the company records the following resolution:

(At) this nexte Courte the Company will make Choice of one whom they will put in (the place of) Howell Jones Deceased, for looking to the walke & water house at Islington And it is ordered that none shalbe there suffered hereafter to sell drink or . . . or to use victualling in any sorte whatsoever.[1]

Although plotting the course and digging the channel for the New River was the achievement that most impressed the public,

---

[1] Quoted in *Trans. Soc. Cymmrodorion*, 1956 (1957), p. 32.

it was only half the work needed to supply London with water. Some months before the opening ceremony at New River Head preliminary steps had been taken to obtain a supply of elms for the mains. On 18 April 1612 John Bartlemew, who was employed later as a pipe-borer, was paid 10s. 'to defraye his charges into Berks to make choyse of Elmes for the use of the worke'; one of the suppliers in that county was an Adventurer, Sir Henry Nevill, of Billingsbear Park, who was paid £67 for elms on the following 6 March. Elms were also obtained from various other places in the counties near London, many of them being brought by river to the 'Bridge House' at Southwark, below London Bridge, where there was a wharf called 'Pipe Borer's Wharf'.[1] Elm-trunks had been in use for water-pipes since Roman times. The pipes were made by placing them on trestles and boring them through with augers turned by horses. The accounts show that pipes of different sizes were made, with bores of 3, 4, or 6 inches in diameter. One end of the pipe was pointed like a pencil, the other end being hollowed out, and joints were made by driving the point of one pipe into the hollow end of the next. Together with John Bartlemew, the chief pipe-borer was Richard Parkes; later this work was in the hands of a man named Avery Lacey. Usually the accounts do not record details of the cost of pipe making, only lump-sum payments, but in March 1623, 162 yards of 3-inch pipe cost 7½d. a yard for boring and jointing. Great care was necessary to avoid splitting the trunks in the process of boring, and iron collars or hoops were inserted to strengthen them at the joints. It has been said that these did not come into use until the eighteenth century,[2] but the New River accounts show that quantities of them were used in Myddelton's time, at a cost of 5d. to 7d. each. The earliest reference to them appears to be in the week ending 4 September 1613, when £15. 10s. was paid 'toe Thomas Cock for Elmes and Hoopes for the pypes'. On 18 May 1616 'V dosen of greate Iron hoopes for the sixe ynche pipes weyeinge a Cxlij[1] att three pence the pounde' cost £1. 15s.

---

[1] Since known as Hay's Wharf. See Aytoun Ellis, *Three Hundred Years on London River* (1952), c. 2.
[2] Aytoun Ellis, op. cit., p. 25.

These wooden mains had a very short life. The bark was left on as some protection against decay, and in a clay soil they might last twenty years, but they often needed replacing in less than five, and almost at once materials of various sorts were in demand to stop leaks. Thus on 20 November 1613 'xvj yardes of Canvas toe make Seareclothes toe mende the pipes' were bought at 6d. a yard, and on 17 December 1614, at a cost of 5s., two 'Bazell skynnes' (i.e. tanned sheepskins). The branch pipes conveying water to consumers' houses were made of lead, and sheet lead, costing 15s. 6d. a hundred pounds, was also used to repair the mains. To effect a junction at the point where a branch, or 'quill' as it was often called, was taken off, brass ferules were driven into the wooden mains. Solder was bought at 8d. a pound to join the tenants' lead pipes to the ferules. Apparently tenants were required at first to make and pay for their own connexions to the mains, and used lead ferules for this, but these were unsatisfactory, and later Myddelton provided brass ones instead. Accordingly Henrie Greene was paid £2. os. 4d. 'for xxij brasse fferrells at xxijd. a pece to putt on the branches where the wooden pipes were decayed and newe ones placed in their Roome and by that means the leaden fferrells wᶜʰ the Tennantes hadd paid for were broken and spoyled and their branches toe short'. Brass was also sometimes used for stopcocks, which were expensive items (a 6-inch stopcock cost £10, a 2-inch one £2. 10s.), and more often the stopcocks were made of wood. In April 1617 Avery Lacey supplied ten, 'toe place in the pipes in severall streetes, att xijs. a pece'.

In spite of their inefficiency, wooden mains continued in use, in London as in other towns, for many years, and they were not generally replaced by cast-iron pipes until early in the nineteenth century. Specimens of them are preserved in one of the corridors of the Metropolitan Water Board's offices, and in many places elsewhere as well.[1] Apart from the drawbacks of their short life, and the loss of water through leakage, wooden pipes could only sustain a fairly low pressure, and the water authorities often did

---

[1] Surviving specimens are generally about 8 or 10 ft. long, with an external diameter of about 2 ft. at one end and 18 in. at the other.

not claim to supply water to the upper floors of houses,[1] nor did they attempt to maintain a constant supply. Wealthier citizens had a cistern in their houses, but many simply had a water-butt in the backyard. The area supplied was divided into districts, and the turncocks went round, opening the valves for what was supposed to be long enough to fill the cisterns and butts, then shutting off the water and passing on to the next district. Each district was supposed to be supplied on three or at least two days a week, but consumers complained that they were often left without water for a week or more. In these circumstances, we gather, the most effective way of getting a supply was to bribe the turncock.[2]

From New River Head the mains were laid first of all across the fields to St. John Street, and then by West Smithfield to Newgate, where they branched. By January 1614 they reached Cheapside in one direction, and went down Old Bailey to Ludgate in the other. In the course of that year extensions were made from Ludgate westward to Temple Bar, and from Newgate up Holborn to Holborn Bars. Branch pipes from these mains were laid to serve the side streets, and in 1617 another line of mains was laid down Goswell Road. The cost of pipe-laying may be gathered from the payment of £3. 6s. 8d. on 5 April 1617 'to Edward Horne for digging and paveing CC yardes att 4d. per yarde toe leye pipes in the streetes'. Pipe-laying was often done at night, by the light of links and candles, costing 4d. a pound or more. Mr. Berry notes that there was no attempt to enter the territory, beyond St. Paul's and Watling Street, served by the London Bridge Waterworks, but John Darge, a small independent supplier, who was said to have 'made lx^li per annum of his water

---

[1] A frequently quoted agreement between Myddelton and one of his tenants, dated 1616 and to run for twenty-one years 'from the feast of the natyvitye of St. John Baptist next ensewinge', provided that in consideration of an annual rent of 26s. 8d. the tenant should have 'a quill or branch of lead containing halfe an inch of water or thereabouts . . . to be convaied in the foresaid pipe of lead by tooe of the smallest swan-necked cockes . . . into the yard and kitchine' of the tenant's dwelling-house (quoted in D. Hughson, London (1809), vi. 358 n., and elsewhere).

[2] Cf. Jnl. Inst. Civil Engineers, vol. 31 (1948), p. 13. Aubrey remarked in 1682 that London had 'growne so populous and big' that the New River Company could 'serve the pipes to private houses but twice a weeke' (Brief Lives, ed. A. Clark, i. 255, ii. 60).

work before the Newe Ryver came', was bought out, very cheapy it would seem. On 2 July 1614 he was given £25. 11s. 'in consideration that hee shall serve noe more water from Fogwell springe, for that hee hathe surrendered all his tenantes to Mr. Myddelltonne, whereby he shall suffer noe greate losse'. His lead pipes were valued by two plumbers, one acting on his behalf, the other on Myddelton's, and he was paid £74. 9s. 'for 322 yards of leaden pipe weighing 27^{li} in a yarde, and 168 yards weighing 14^{li} in a yarde'.

Many entries in the accounts are concerned with the wages and other expenses for digging the trenches for the pipes, hauling the pipes through the streets (this was done on pairs of coach-wheels), and clearing away the rubbish; these items, together with the cost of purchasing the elms and making them into pipes, actually amounted to more than the cost of constructing the New River itself. Grossly exaggerated estimates of the cost of the whole undertaking have been repeated, one writer putting it as high as £500,000,[1] but the account books show that in fact the total expenditure, down to the end of November 1614, amounted to £18,525. 0s. 1d., and of this two-thirds were spent in the years 1613 and 1614.[2] According to the agreement made with James I, the King was to meet half the expenses, and he had duly made a first payment of £569. 17s. 11d. on 26 August 1612. Myddelton then got two instalments of £1,000 each on 17 and 22 February 1613, £242. 19s. 5½d. on 21 April, and another £1,000 on 25 June. After this, payments were made in instalments

---

[1] This figure was given ('as it is recorded'!) by J. Entick, *History and Survey of London* (1761), pp. 112–14. The New River Company took advantage of this figure and quoted it in an 'Address to Occupiers of Houses' which they issued in 1821; but this was propaganda at a time of acute controversy over the London water-supply. W. Matthews, in a work published in 1835 (*Hydraulia*, p. 57), thought the original cost of the undertaking must have been between £100,000 and £200,000, but as W. R. Scott pointed out (*Constitution and Finance of . . . Joint-Stock Companies . . .* iii. 21–22) these exaggerated estimates failed to take account of the changes in the rates of wages and the cost of materials since the early seventeenth century. Scott was the first to give the correct figure, though he did not find out how it was made up. Samuel Smiles was misled by the misprint in *Cal. S.P.D.* (see p. 65, n. 1), and mistook the whole for a part; yet by adding it to the other parts he arrived at a total which was not far wrong. W. Maitland (*History of London* (1739), p. 629) was unusual in considerably underestimating the cost.

[2] Details are summarized by Mr. G. C. Berry in *Trans. Soc. Cymmrodorion*, 1956 (1957), p. 41.

of varying amounts every few months or so until 24 July 1615, by which time he had received a total of £8,347. 4s. 10½d. The exchequer authorities evidently decided to regard the undertaking as complete by November 1614, and all they paid was half the expenditure incurred up to that date—a total of £9,262. 9s. 6d.; even so Myddelton had to wait until 1617 before he got the balance of £915. 4s. 7½d. still due to him.[1] Actually there were still quite considerable outgoings on repairs and maintenance of the existing works, apart from alterations and extensions—the 'Boarded River' at Highbury, for example, was built in 1618–19—but the King's contributions towards these expenses were left to be met out of the profits, when they should arise. With his capital thus locked up, and much of it indeed literally buried underground, it is not surprising that Myddelton found himself short of money, and on 6 September 1614 he asked the city authorities for a loan of £3,000. The corporation, 'entering into consideration of the great benefitt this Citty is likely to receave and enioye by bringing of his water to this citty and of the reasonableness of his request', agreed to make him the loan, at 6 per cent. interest, on security entered by Myddelton himself, the Lord Mayor, Robert Myddelton, and Robert Bateman.[2] Myddelton named a period of three years, but the loan was still outstanding at his death.

In fact, as a profit-making concern, the New River in its early years proved very disappointing. For many years there appears to have been a widespread prejudice against piped water, in favour of water brought round in the old-fashioned way by water-carriers, and this seems to have persisted even when the water they carried actually came from the New River. As late as the early nineteenth century a writer remembered

the prejudices of old-fashioned people in favour of water brought to the door, and their sympathy with the complaints of the water-bearer.

---

[1] Actually this was 6½d. short. Detailed receipts are given in Myddelton's statement in L.R. 2/34. The total (£9,262. 9s. 6d., misprinted £2,262, but corrected in manuscript in the Bodleian Library copy) is confirmed in Cal. S.P.D. 1611–18, p. 365. It is repeated in Cal. S.P.D. 1631–3, p. 160. Of the balance due £500 was paid on 20 Mar. 1617, and the last £415. 4s. 7½d. on 22 Sept. Some details of the King's payments may be found in F. Devon, Issues of the Exchequer . . . during the Reign of James I (1836), pp. 156, 172, 190.   [2] City Records, Repertories 31–2/396.

'Fresh and fair new River-water! none of your pipe sludge!' vociferated the water-bearer. 'Ah dear!' cried his customers, 'Ah dear! Well, what'll the world come to!—they won't let poor people live at all by and by—here they're breaking up the ground, and we shall all be under water some day or other with their goings on—I'll stick to the carrier as long as he has a pail-full and I've a penny, and when we haven't we must all go to the workhouse together'. This was the talk and reasoning of many honest people within my recollection, who preferred taxing themselves to the daily payment of a penny and often twopence to the water-carrier, in preference to having 'Company's water' at eighteen shillings per annum. Persons of this order of mind [he commented] were neither political economists nor domestic economists: they were, for the most part, simple and kind-hearted souls, who illustrated the ancient saying that 'the destruction of the poor is their poverty'—they have perished for 'lack of knowledge'.[1]

At any rate, there was no eagerness on the part of consumers to take 'Myddelton's water', and after an initial spurt from a small beginning, the number of tenants increased only slowly. At Midsummer 1614 there were 37 of them; this figure had risen to 175 by Michaelmas, and 351 by Christmas, but at Lady Day 1615 it was only 384, and it was not till Michaelmas 1618 that the number of tenants exceeded 1,000. A 'fine', or premium, was charged when the supply was first laid on, and a quarterly rent of either 5s. or 6s. 8d. John Milton's father was one of the tenants: another was Myddelton himself, who paid 10s. a quarter for his house in Wood Street. The total receipts during the first year, from Midsummer 1614 to Lady Day 1615, were £995. 9s. 8d., made up of £396. 4s. 8d. rents, £19. 16s. 8d. arrears, and £579. 8s. 4d. fines. Meanwhile, apart from wages, there were continual outgoings on upkeep and repairs; the amount of arrears and bad debts increased, and for a long time there seemed little prospect of the concern making a profit.

---

[1] W. Horne, *The Table Book* (1827), 1859 edn. i. 733–4. The water-carriers had tried to oppose the New River from the start, and the account books record that in August 1611 2s. 6d. was paid for a warrant 'to bringe a seditious fellowe . . . who persuaded the water bearers of London to petition to his Matie against the newe Ryver' before the Recorder (Sir Henry Montagu).

Apart from the citizens' reluctance to pay for having water piped to their houses (after all, the old conduits supplied water free of charge), the undertaking also suffered from thoughtless vandalism and deliberate dishonesty such as public authorities only too often have had (and still have) cause to complain of. On 19 June 1615 the Privy Council referred to

'many abuses and misdemeanors daylie comitted and done, in and upon the said river, by lewde and ill-disposed people, in cuttinge the bankes and letting out the said water, to the inconvenience and prejudice of the tennantes, castinge in dogges and filth, and lettinge in sewers and other fowle and uncleane water, to the annoyance of the said water; breakinge and carrieinge away the bridges, vaultes and rayles standinge in and uppon the river; takinge and carryinge water out of the said river in lickquer cartes, tubbes or barrells, and stealing branches and cockes from the pipes without any composicion, togeather with many such like abuses and annoyances. . . .'

Offenders were to be brought before the Council 'to answeare to their misdemeanors in that behalfe, whereof they may be assured his Majestie wilbe very sensible, beinge to the prejudice of soe worthie a worke, wherein his Highnes is so deeply interested'.[1]

The river was regularly patrolled by the walksmen, but obviously they could not entirely check such misbehaviour.[2] When the New River Company's charter was issued it contained clauses prohibiting people from throwing or putting into the river 'anie earth, rubbish, soyle, gravell, stones, dogges, Catts, or anie Cattle, Carrion, or anie unwholesome or uncleane thinge'. Among other forbidden practices were washing 'clothes, wooll, or other thinge' in the river, damaging or breaking down the banks, bridges, &c., or doing anything to 'hinder, lett, stopp, or annoye the said water, or the current or passage thereof'; allowing any 'sincke, sewer, ditche, Tanhowse, dying howse, or seege' to flow into the river; and drawing off any water from the river without licence. No 'new ditch, pond, pitt, or Trench' was to be dug near the New River, 'whereby the water of the same may

---

[1] *Acts P.C. 1615–16*, pp. 212–13.

[2] In 1644 the company complained of the conduct of 'sundry ill disposed and disaffected persons', who had 'dammed up the passage of the river, cut the banks', &c. (H.M.C. *6th Report*, p. 18*b*).

fall or drayne away', nor were any 'sallowes, willowes, or Elme' to be planted or set within five yards of the channel.

As the year 1616 passed, and still no profits were in sight, the King decided that pressure must be put on the citizens of London, and on 22 December the Privy Council addressed a letter to the Lord Mayor and aldermen. After a recital of Myddelton's statutory powers and his achievement as the city's deputy (although 'unless his Majesty had been graciously pleased to favour and supporte his undertakinge, he had suncke under the waight of that burthen'), and an allusion to the King having allowed 'the passage of that water through his parke', the letter reminds the city that the purpose of the venture was 'the generall good and proffitt of that citty, as well in the use of sweete and holesome water as for the preservacion of the same from casualty and dainger of fyre, whereof there hath been good experience three severall tymes this last sommer'. Nevertheless, the King had been informed, 'but few, in respect of the generallytie and such for whome it was principally intended, doe take that water', and it was not to be supposed that two Acts of Parliament and an Act of Common Council that so much concerned the health and safety of the city had been passed 'to noe use or purpose other than the hinderance and prejudice of such as were by yow deputed to undertake the same'. His Majesty therefore had commanded 'and accordingly wee doe require your Lordship and the rest to order and provide . . . that the said water may be taken into all such houses within that citty and the liberties as either out of necessity or convenience may make use of the same . . .'.[1]

What Myddelton himself thought of these dictatorial proceedings we can only surmise. He may have approved of them, and may even have asked for the King's support. But he was himself a citizen of London, and a liveryman of one of its greatest companies, and he must have known (as indeed the King must also), that the corporation had no legal powers to compel Londoners to take his water. On the whole it seems more likely that the initiative was the King's, though it is true that some five years

[1] *Acts P.C. Aug. 1616–Dec. 1617*, pp. 99–100; W. H. and H. C. Overall, *Analytical Index to . . . Remembrancia* (1878), pp. 556–7.

later the Adventurers were anxious to enlist the use of the King's prerogative powers to expedite the collection of arrears.[1] Be that as it may, on this occasion the practical results of the King's action seem to have been small, but before long he intervened again.

In January 1617 certain brewers, George Beale and others in the parish of St. Giles without Cripplegate, asked the City Lands Committee for a lease of the Dowgate conduit. They offered to maintain and serve the conduit with water, relieving the city of the cost of pumping and repairs, provided they might have permission to lay pipes to convey the surplus water to their brewhouses. The Lands Committee thought this a reasonable request, but in view of the King's recent orders they referred it to the Common Council, with a recommendation that it should be granted, on the understanding 'that the petitioners were willing to take in Middleton's water for their other uses and to pay reasonable rents for the same'.[2] The King, however, was not satisfied unless the New River had a complete monopoly, and on 27 February another letter came from the Lords of the Council to the Lord Mayor and aldermen. It referred to 'his Majestie's pleasure and comaundement', to which they did not doubt that due regard would be had, 'signified upon the like occasion heeretofore for the stay of a house intended to be erected on London Bridge for the conveying of water into Southworke to the prejudice of his Majestie's waterworke at Islington', and declared that 'the new streame, brought from the springes of Amwell and Chaudwell at an extreame and excessive charge', was 'of great consequence for his Majestie's service', and deserved 'all due favore and encouragement'. Therefore they 'thought it expedient to pray and require' that the Dowgate proposal should be rejected, the more so since the brewers could be 'plentifully served with water from the new streame comeinge to Islington and conveyed from thence by pipes into the citty'.[3]

The King's next idea was to suggest that he might take over the whole concern, and on 9 March 1618 Sir Robert Mansell, Sir

[1] See below, p. 77. [2] W.H. and H. C. Overall, op. cit., pp. 557–8.
[3] Ibid., and *Acts P.C. Jan. 1618–June 1619*, p. 54.

Giles Mompesson, Sir John Hippisley, and Thomas Carmon were instructed 'to summon the Adventurers . . . and treat with them to find out at what rate of yearly pension each Adventurer in the Undertaking will deliver up his share to the king'.[1] Nothing apparently came of this, and on the face of it it seems odd that the King should have wished to be more deeply involved in an unprofitable concern. The idea was still in his mind a year later, however, when the Privy Council put forward alternative proposals. 'The new streame of water brought from the springes of Amwell and Chaudwell to the citty of London', the Council wrote, had 'not sorted to that effect as was expected, either in pointe of profitt or otherwise, forasmuch as his Majestie hath a moitie therein'; and in the hope that there might be 'some course thought upon for the better improvement of the said streame to his Majesty's advauntage either by taking it whollie into his Majesty's hands or otherwise by letting it whollie to such undertakers as have the other moytie at a rent to his Majestie', Mr. Secretary Naunton, the Chancellor of the Exchequer, the Master of the Rolls, and Sir Edward Coke were instructed to open discussions with Sir Giles Mompesson, Hugh Myddelton, 'and such others as they shall thinke meete to be dealt with concerning that busines'.[2]

Ultimately, in the reign of Charles I, the second of these alternatives was adopted, but the immediate outcome of the negotiations was the grant of a charter of incorporation, dated 21 June 1619, to the twenty-nine Adventurers, under the name of 'The Governor and Company of the New River brought from Chadwell and Amwell to London'.[3] Hugh Myddelton was named as the first Governor, with Robert Bateman, Skinner, as Deputy Governor, and Rowland Backhouse, Mercer, as Treasurer. The remaining twenty-six Adventurers included seven members of Hugh Myddelton's family—his brother Sir Thomas (formerly

---

[1] Sackville MSS. (H.M.C.), no. 505 (M 1008).
[2] *Acts P.C. Jan. 1618–June 1619*, pp. 157, 158.
[3] Patent Roll, 17 James I, part xvi, no. 67, dated 21 June 1619. The original is now at the office of the New River Co. Ltd. in Myddelton Square, St. John St., E.C. 1. The text is printed in Selden Soc., vol. 28 (1913), pp. 106–17, and in R. Sisley, *The London Water Supply* (1899), Appendix A, pp. 161–71.

Lord Mayor); his son and heir Hugh and his younger son (and successor) William, Goldsmith; his nephews William Myddelton, Draper, and Richard Myddelton, Grocer; Henry Myddelton, son and heir of David Myddelton 'late of London, Gentleman, deceased'; and Timothy Myddelton, Esquire. Besides these there were Sir Henry Montagu, Lord Chief Justice, Sir Robert Killigrew, Sir William Burlacie the elder and Sir William Burlacie the younger, Sir Lawrence Hyde and Nicholas Hyde 'of the Middle Temple . . . Esquire', Sir Henry Nevill, John Packer, Samuel Backhouse and his son and heir John, Humphrey Hall, Girdler, Peter Vanlore, 'Merchant Stranger', Marmaduke Rawdon, Clothworker, Henry Vincent, Leatherseller, William Bateman, Grocer,[1] John Farrer, Skinner, Edward Prichard, Skinner, James Bearblock, Gentleman, and Gabriel Newman, Goldsmith. In consideration of his 'long travail and attendance . . . about the said waterworke', William Lewyn, who had kept the accounts since 1611, was to be the first clerk of the company, with a right to hold this office, either in person or by deputy ('he behaving himself well and honestly in the execution of the same'), for life.[2]

The constitution of the company was unusual ('unique', according to Scott),[3] because the King could not incorporate himself, yet the arrangement by which he held a moiety of the concern was retained, and only the other moiety was the property of the Adventurers. At the same time the King had no part in the management of the company's affairs. All he had, to look after his interests, was an observer with a right to be present at the company's meetings and to inspect its accounts. This office, with the title 'Surveyor of the New River', was granted by the King for life to Edward Ball.[4] Since 1617 it had been his signature, in

[1] Hugh Myddelton's nephew by marriage: his wife Jane was the daughter of Hugh's younger brother Robert. Sir Henry Montagu, previously Recorder of London, became Lord Chief Justice after the dismissal of Sir Edward Coke.

[2] Years later he complained that he had been wrongly dispossessed by a certain Josias Barnes, and petitioned Charles I for reinstatement, which after inquiry was granted him (*Cal. S.P.D. 1636–7*, p. 170). The Myddelton family connexion persisted for a long time after Sir Hugh's death. John Grene (or Greene), who was clerk of the company for many years in the seventeenth century, married Elizabeth, daughter of Sir Hugh's son William, who succeeded him as Governor.

[3] *Joint Stock Companies*, iii. 22.

[4] *Cal. S.P.D. 1611–18*, p. 517 (19 Jan. 1618).

succession to Miles Whitacres', that had appeared in the accounts, jointly with Hugh Myddelton's, in attestation of their correctness. The King apparently created a sinecure duplicate of this office in favour of Sir Giles Mompesson, who had participated in the negotiations that preceded the grant of the company's charter, for he was appointed 'surveyor of the profits' of the company at a fee of £200 per annum out of the King's moiety of the profits.[1] For the present these were nil, but we gather that Mompesson had drawn £250 by the time he was disgraced and fled the country in 1621.[2] Ball remained in office, at a salary of £100 a year, and when Charles I later surrendered the royal moiety it was stipulated that the company should pay Ball an annuity of £100 for life.[3]

The undertaking had originally been entirely in Myddelton's hands, but some time previously—exactly when is uncertain, but presumably at an early date, when he found it necessary to enlist the support of partners—he had divided it into thirty-six shares, and these continued to be held by the twenty-nine Adventurers. According to Scott, the 'par value' of each of these shares in the Adventurers' moiety was £257. 5s. 9⅝d., but this figure[4] bears no relation to the amounts of the Adventurers' original contributions, which had been made long before. Sir Henry Nevill, for example, who took two shares on 8 May 1612, paid £200 for them, but again this does not mean that the original value of a New River share was £100. The Adventurers undertook a liability for further contributions, and Nevill in particular undertook to pay a sixteenth of all charges when expenditure exceeded £3,200.[5]

Meetings of the Adventurers were held in various places. The first was in Sir Henry Montagu's chambers in Serjeants' Inn; other meetings took place at Hugh Myddelton's house.[6] At the beginning of the eighteenth century the company's office was at

[1] *Cal. S.P.D. 1619–23*, p. 91 (9 Nov. 1619).

[2] B.M. Add. MS. 29774, f. 61 *verso*.   [3] *Cal. S.P.D. 1631–3*, p. 182.

[4] Arrived at by dividing half the cost of the undertaking (i.e. the amount the King contributed, £9,262. 9s. 6d.) by 36.

[5] *Trans. Soc. Cymmrodorion*, 1956 (1957), p. 30, and see above, p. 37, n. 3.

[6] Ibid., p. 43.

Puddle Dock, whence they moved to Bridewell Precinct; ultimately their headquarters were established at New River Head. The house there underwent various alterations in the course of years, and now no longer exists, but the late seventeenth-century oak-panelled court-room it contained, with the arms of Myddelton and Greene[1] on the ceiling, has been rebuilt, on an upstairs floor, into the great block of offices for the Metropolitan Water Board that now stands on the site.

[1] Cf. p. 71, n. 2, above.

V

THE NEW RIVER COMPANY

As the number of consumers gradually increased, it became necessary to supplement the supply of water from the Chadwell and Amwell springs, and one of the first actions of the newly founded company was to tap the River Lea itself. On 17 June 1620 the accounts contain items of 10s. 'for twentie piles, toe make a damme in the Wheyre [i.e. Ware] Ryver, toe tourne in the streame to the Ryver att vjd. a pce', and 8s. 'for a hundred of wharfinge boordes for the same'. This action met with opposition from the bargemen on the Lea, and the dam which had been erected a short distance above Ware was removed. Before long, however, it was set up again, and a channel was cut across the flat meadow to carry water from the Lea into the adjacent New River just below the Chadwell spring. Disputes recurred about the abstraction of water from the Lea, until in 1738, after litigation, an Act of Parliament was passed, which laid down how much water the company might take, what conditions were to be observed, and what compensation was to be paid.[1] Even so disputes continued, and the question was not finally settled until, following the enactment of the River Lee Water Act in 1855, the 'New Gauge' was established at the intake in 1856.

It was not only the Lea bargemen who regarded the company with disfavour. Monopolies were a notorious grievance in the early seventeenth century, and the New River Company under its royal patronage was no exception. The company wanted to have statutory confirmation of its charter, but a Bill to confirm the powers and privileges conferred by the King's letters patent

---

[1] J. Nelson, *History and Antiquities of the Parish of Islington* (1823), p. 161; S. Lewis, *History and Topography of the Parish of St. Mary, Islington* (1842), p. 426. On one occasion, when the New River Co. wanted to take more water, their engineer is said to have offered to pay double the price if a pipe of double the diameter were installed, to which the agent for the R. Lea authority agreed, not realizing, in his ignorance of mathematics, that he was thus allowing four times as much water to be drawn off.

did not get beyond its first reading in the Commons (7 May 1621).[1] Three years later another attempt was made to secure an Act of Parliament for this purpose. This second Bill won the approval of Sir Edward Coke, on whose motion it was sent to committee, with the comment that it would prevent 'one great mischief that hangs over the city—*nimia potatio: frequens incendium*'; but after that no more was heard of it.[2] The House had just rejected a Bill for confirming the King's charter to the Company of Gold Wire Drawers of the City of London, on the ground that it was undesirable to confirm a monopoly by Act of Parliament, and probably the New River Company's Bill suffered for the same reason. Eighteen years later the company hopefully tried again, but the date on which their third Bill received its first reading (3 May 1642),[3] with the outbreak of the Civil War in the offing, was scarcely propitious, and in any case the Long Parliament was unlikely to approve of a measure designed to benefit a concern which was supposed to enjoy royal favour.

Not long after the incorporation of the company a change was made in the arrangements for Myddelton's own remuneration. He had himself been responsible from the beginning for all expenditure, and since January 1612 he had drawn a personal allowance of £2. 6s. 8d. a week. Henceforward he was to receive a comprehensive fee of £800 a year, drawn at half-yearly intervals, the first £400 being paid on 30 January 1622. In return for this he undertook to manage and maintain the existing works, but not to pay for extensions. Nor was he responsible for such expenses as those involved in visits of inspection by parties of Adventurers. When, for example, on 26 March 1625, £8. 17s. was spent 'for the chardges for dyett and horse Meate for those that were appointed to Survey the state of the Ryver from London to Ware there beinge tenne in Nomber, and tenne horses, they being three dayes uppon the same Surveye', it appears as a

---

[1] *C.J.* i. 611. The powers which Myddelton had exercised on the city's behalf had been conferred on the city by statute, and from a legal point of view it no doubt seemed desirable that the transfer of these powers to the company should be confirmed by statute, instead of resting only on letters patent.

[2] First reading 4 March 1624 (*C.J.* i. 727); committed 22 March (ibid. 745).

[3] *C.J.* ii. 554.

separate entry in the accounts. Myddelton must soon have found £800 insufficient, for on 30 September 1622 his half-yearly fee was raised to £450, and on 26 March 1623 to £500, at which it remained until his death. The same responsibility and remuneration then passed to his widow: the last two half-yearly payments recorded in the accounts (30 September 1631 to 25 March 1632, and 26 March 1632 to 30 September 1632) are of £500 'to the Ladie Myddelton', 'for the meynetenance of the waterworkes'.

Meanwhile the King, apparently dissatisfied with the way the company was being run, was still hopeful of making more out of it if he could get it wholly into his own hands. He appointed a body of commissioners, who were instructed (28 May 1622) to summon the Adventurers to a meeting 'and to treate with them at what rate of yearly pensions they will accept severally for their portions in the said Woorke'. The commissioners were 'also to see howe the monies are expended upon the Woork and what is further necessarie to be donn for the good and continuation of the same'. From reports made by one of the commissioners, Sir William Pitt, Teller of the Exchequer and Commissioner of the Navy, we gather that they held their first meeting with the Adventurers on 10 July.[1] The Adventurers, however, were not disposed to be co-operative, and this and subsequent meetings were inconclusive. Nevertheless, the undertaking was at last beginning to pay its way, and in his final report, dated 13 February 1623, Pitt was able to announce that the accounts for the year up to Michaelmas 1622 showed the sum of £433. 2s. 7d. as due to the King, 'being the first summ to be paid to his Ma^{ty} since the beginning of the Workes'.[2] For the current year he reckoned that the King ought to be entitled, as a return on his moiety, to the sum of £772. 4s. (half of £1,544. 8s., a figure arrived at by

[1] B.M. Add. MS. 29974, f. 63. It was about this time (June 1622) that the King, when knighting the Lord Mayor, told him, among other things, to 'attend to Middleton's water' (*Cal. S.P.D. 1619–23*, p. 409). Samuel Smiles connected this with the King's accident in the New River the previous January, but this is a supposition not warranted by the evidence. More likely the King was telling the Lord Mayor to press Londoners to take in the water.

[2] Ibid., f. 61 *verso*. This was the net amount due to the King, after deducting what he owed (£370. 17s. 10d.) as his contribution towards the outgoings. Whether the King actually received this amount seems doubtful: the figure recorded in *S.P.D. James I*, clviii. 59 (S.P. 14/158) as the income from the 'New water workes' in 1623 is only £325. It is prudently entered under the heading 'casuall and uncertaine'.

deducting 'the annuall charge for maynetenance of the woorkes', which he put at £1,300, from the yield from rents, estimated to amount to £2,844. 8s.),[1] but he had to admit that 'parte is unpaid and some hard to be gotten'. Even 'if all were recovered, nay if all the shares were bought in at reasonable rates', he doubted 'whether by any course to bee taken without more pressure than the tymes will beare, a savinge bargaine can be made to bring the works to perfeccōn and so to maintaine them and withall to answere his Maties 9000 li. stocke'.[2]

In any case he saw 'noe hope to bringe the sharers to any reasonable composicion'; he had managed to get them to meet and discuss the matter, 'yet their answere was still dilatorie'. They argued that 'their shares for the present did arise but to 28 li. a man', and they 'could not sell them at that rate without too great loss. That if his Maiestie by regall power and proclamacōn would assist them they might then be raised to 100 li. a peece: and then they might affoord a good bargaine'. This, however, would not benefit the King, for 'by the condicōns obtained in their Incorporacōn they have gotten this advantage that his Maties moytie being undevided from theirs cannot be improved without improving theirs. And they being manie the losse of their moitie devided in manie parts wilbee easier to be borne than his Ma^ts which fals upon himself. Howe to drive them from this hold wee yet see no meanes.' It might seem reasonable 'to remove interruptions by suffering them in his [the King's] name to prosecute offenders by informacōn in the Exchequer and by levying their Arrerages by Pursevaunts or such other legall courses as the Councell learned should devise'. Nevertheless he did not believe that 'the workes would be raised to that profitt which they promise to themselves'. He dared not advise the King to allow them 'their owne desires to use the power of Proclamacōn', as he feared that this would lead only to 'fines and vexacōn' rather than 'reforming therby or improving the workes'.[3]

---

[1] B.M. Add. MS. 29974, f. 64, which contains a detailed statement of rents, arrears, and outgoings for the year 1622. Cf. also statements in L.R. 2/33 and 2/34 (P.R.O.) and Sackville MSS., no. 7841 (H.M.C.).

[2] i.e. the King's original contribution of £9,262. 9s. 6d.

[3] B.M. Add. MS. 29974, f. 61.

The Adventurers were undoubtedly right in estimating that
the value of their shares had suffered a heavy depreciation, for the
profit just shown represented a much smaller return on the capital
sunk in the undertaking than could reasonably be expected in
view of the risk involved. Nor could the outlook for the future
be described as bright, and for years the company was seriously
hampered by a load of arrears and bad debts. For Myddelton
himself, however, there came well-deserved personal reward,
first from the King, who on 19 October 1622 made him a baronet
in recognition of his various achievements as an engineer,[1] and
in the following year from the City of London. On 13 November
1623 the Court of Aldermen put on record 'the great and extra-
ordinarie benefitt and service this Cittye receiveth by the water
brought through the streets of the same by the travaile and in-
dustrye of Sir Hugh Middleton . . . , especially att many great fires
happened within this Citty, and Chefely the last night at a verie
terrible and fearefull fire which might have greatly endangered the
Cittye, had that needefull water binn wanting'.[2]

This fire had started in the evening among some flax in one of
the warehouses belonging to Alderman Sir William Cockayne,
in Broad Street, 'and ceased not till two of the clocke the next
morning, in which space it burnt his whole house and three of his
neighbours' houses, to the great damage and danger of many
neere Inhabitants, and to the great fright and terrour of the whole
Citie'. As soon as Myddelton became aware of the fire he 'caused
all the Scluces of the Water Cesterne in the field to be let open
whereby there was plenty of water to quench the fire', and we
gather that this was not the first time that the New River water
had been of service in this way.[3] In those days London was largely
built of wood, and with its narrow streets it is remarkable that
the famous disaster of 1666 had not occurred years previously.
On this occasion the Court of Aldermen 'out of their love and
good respect to the said Sir Hugh Middleton, for that his worthy
and famous worke', decided to 'bestowe uppon him a Chayne of

---

[1] See above, Chapter I.
[2] City Records, Repertories 38/12a.
[3] E. Howes, *Continuation of John Stow's Annales or a Generall Chronicle of England*
(1631), p. 1035b.

Gould of the value of two hundred markes, as a token of their love and kinde remembrance'.[1] The chain was set with diamonds, with a pendant bearing the arms of the city, and as a goldsmith Sir Hugh himself supervised the making of it.[2] He is shown wearing this chain and pendant in his portrait by Cornelius Johnson.

Meanwhile the finances of the New River Company continued to languish. In 1625, the year of King James's death, there was a serious outbreak of plague in the city, and according to a contemporary account over 35,000 people lost their lives.[3] As a result, there was a decline in the number of the company's tenants, arrears of water-rents increased, and recovery was slow. It was not long before King Charles became convinced that the royal moiety in the New River was not worth keeping, and he began negotiations for a different arrangement with the company, on the lines of one of the suggestions made on his father's behalf some years previously.[4] Another motive for extricating himself from the company may have been the promotion of a new scheme to bring water to London from springs at Hoddesdon. This was first mooted as early as March 1627, when Nicholas Saunder, Henry Saunder, and Michael Parker were granted powers to carry out the scheme, undertaking in return to pay the Crown a rent of £4,000 a year.[5] It is hard to take this ludicrous figure seriously, but the King was apparently captivated by the prospect of making so much money simply by granting patents. We hear no more of the two Saunders, but three years later Michael Parker, described as 'of London, gentleman', had found fresh partners in Sir Edward Stradling, of St. Donat's in the county of Glamorgan, Knight, and John Lyde, of Horspath in the county of Oxford, Esquire. On 11 February 1631 these three entered into an indenture with Charles I, in which they undertook to bring the water from the Hoddesdon springs 'in an aqueduct of stone or brick, that being the cleanest and wholesomest way to carry or bring the same in its own native puritie'; the rent of £4,000 a year

---

[1] City Records, Repertories, loc. cit.

[2] R. R. Sharpe, *London and the Kingdom* (1894), ii. 26 (citing City Records, Letter Book, ii. 51a).

[3] 35,417 in the city, liberties, and outparishes (Howes, op. cit., p. 1041b).

[4] Cf. above, p. 70.   [5] *Cal. S.P.D. 1627–8*, p. 114.

would come 'out of the Yssues and profitts of the said water-works or aqueduct'. It was stipulated that the partners were not to 'diminish any of the springs, or take away any of the water' already brought to London by Sir Hugh Myddelton 'or by any other water-work now in being and in use'; but if the scheme had materialized it would have been bound to compete with the New River.[1]

The scheme hung fire for several years, and in the end it came to nothing, but not for want of perseverance by its promoters or of support by the King. Early in 1639 important persons, including Laud, Coventry, and Juxon, were appointed commissioners for arranging terms with owners and occupiers of the land to be traversed by the aqueduct, a lottery was organized to raise the capital required (estimated at £25,000), and by the autumn of 1639, when a fresh indenture was entered into with the King, nearly half this sum was said to be in hand. Before long, however, the scheme ran into difficulties. Sir Walter Roberts, who had been appointed to manage the work, found himself in trouble, financial and otherwise,[2] and there was also opposition from Sir Edward Forde, who challenged the feasibility of the Hoddesdon scheme and proposed instead to tap the River Colne at Rickmansworth and bring water from there to London in 'a navigable river'. Disputes, petitions, appeals, and hearings in the Lords followed, and in 1641 the promoters of both schemes published pamphlets against each other. In one of these[3] the superiority of the Hoddesdon water was emphasized, and 'Middleton's water', on account of 'the foulnesse and muddinesse of it (coming in an open trench)', was said to be 'found by experience not to be fit for many uses, and to faile for a whole weeke or fortnight together'. This was quite possibly true, and London was growing so rapidly that soon,

[1] Rymer, *Foedera*, xix. 244–9; *Cal. S.P.D. 1629–31*, p. 555.

[2] *Cal. S.P.D. 1638–9*, pp. 304, 314; ibid. *1639*, p. 481; ibid. *1639–40*, pp. 123, 438.

[3] *A Proposition for the serving and supplying of London and Westminster, and other places adjoyning; with a sufficient quantity of good and cleare spring water, to be brought from Hoddesdon in Hartfordshire in a close Aqueduct of Bricke, Stone, Lead, or Timber.* The author was presumably Sir Walter Roberts, or one of his supporters; he also wrote *An Answer to Mr. Fords Booke, entituled A Designe for bringing a Navigable River from Rickmansworth in Hartfordshire to St. Gyles in the Fields* (1641). Annexed is a woodcut showing the route proposed for the aqueduct.

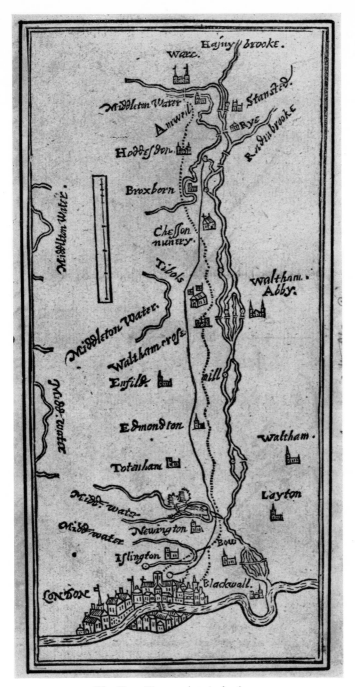

The New River and a rival scheme

apart from its quality, a much greater quantity of water would be needed than Myddelton's New River could supply. In the early 1630's, however, it may well have looked as if under Charles I the New River Company would be exposed to serious competition. James I had discouraged rival concerns, but his son seemed ready to foster them; moreover, Myddelton's health was failing, and in these circumstances it may well have seemed advisable to come to terms with the King.

The basis of the agreement was that the King conveyed his moiety to Sir Hugh Myddelton, in return for a covenant by Sir Hugh, guaranteeing to the Crown a perpetual annuity of £500. The King also agreed to remit all the arrears due to him, amounting in 1631 to £1,290. 0s. 4d., and in return for this concession Myddelton undertook that the annuity should be back-dated to Michaelmas 1630.[1] This liability, which became known as the Crown Clog, or King's Clog, was undertaken by Myddelton personally, and did not fall on the company, which continued to consist only of the holders of the 36 Adventurers' shares. The King's moiety was also divided into 36 shares, which became known as King's shares, but when this division was made is uncertain. It may possibly date back to the original bargain with James I. The report of the commission appointed in 1622, which describes the organization of the company, after referring to the Adventurers' shares, goes on to say 'and the King hath 36 shares more';[2] and Sir William Myddelton, the second baronet, who took on the King's moiety after his father's death, was stated to be 'seized of the King's Moiety ... consisting of 36 shares' in 1646.[3] On the other hand, this expression may only mean that the King's moiety was equivalent to 36 shares, for Sir Hugh's will is worded as if only the Adventurers' moiety was divided into shares.[4] There is no mention of any sale of shares in

[1] *Cal. S.P.D. 1631–3*, p. 178 (4 Nov. 1631). A year's annuity was thus payable immediately. The conveyance of the King's moiety to Myddelton was dated 15 Nov. 1631 (ibid. p. 182).

[2] B.M. Add. MS. 29974, f. 61: see above, p. 76.

[3] In the report of the case *Dame Flora Backhouse* v. *Simon Middleton and others*, 22 Charles II, in *Cases argued and decreed in the High Court of Chancery* (2nd edn., 1707), p. 173.

[4] Below, p. 132. A memorandum drawn up in 1665 also speaks of the King having

the King's moiety until 1657, when Sir Hugh, the third baronet, bargained to sell fourteen of them.[1] Later, both Adventurers' and King's shares were freely bought and sold, and subdivided into fractions, and by the middle of the eighteenth century the Crown Clog had come to fall on $1\frac{1}{2}$ Adventurers' shares and only $29\frac{1}{8}$ King's shares, but exactly how and when this came about is obscure. Scott's attribution of it to the first Sir Hugh is quite imaginary.[2]

The Crown did not long retain its £500 annuity. Soon after the Restoration Charles II granted it for thirty-one years to John Robinson of London, and in June 1661, on Robinson surrendering it, it was granted to John Buckworth, merchant.[3] Two years later Sir Hugh Myddelton, the third baronet, asked for the reversion of it, but did not get it; instead it was promised, on the termination of Buckworth's tenure, to Sir Edward Villiers's daughter Eleanor, and it remained thereafter in private hands.[4] The distinction between the Adventurers' shares and the King's shares was retained throughout the history of the company, and as the holders of King's shares continued to be outside the incorporation, without the power of voting for officers of the company, and were liable for their portions of the Crown Clog, the King's shares commanded a lower market value. In the company's later, more prosperous years, however, the difference was relatively small, and in the course of time the value of both classes of share appreciated enormously.[5]

one half, which he had let in fee farm to Sir Hugh Myddelton for £500 a year, 'the other half being divided into 36 shares' (*Cal. S.P.D. 1664–5*, p. 324).

[1] Below, p. 138.

[2] W. R. Scott, *Joint Stock Companies*, iii. 24. Later the Clog was charged on 2 Adventurers' shares and 29 King's shares.

[3] *Cal. S.P.D. 1660–1*, pp. 328, 522; *Cal. S.P.D. 1661–2*, p. 24.

[4] *Cal. S.P.D. 1663–4*, pp. 219, 611; *Cal. S.P.D. 1664–5*, p. 118. Some particulars about the later history of the Crown Clog may be read in the report of a case tried in 1908, *Adair* v. *New River Co. Ltd. and the Metropolitan Water Board* (25 T.L.R. 193). William III assigned the annuity to a man named Cooling, and it ultimately became vested in the plaintiff. The question in dispute was whether, after the New River Co.'s water undertaking had been transferred to the Metropolitan Water Board by the Metropolis Water Act (1902), the King's Clog, which at some date in the past had been reduced to £400 annually, was payable by the company or by the Board. The Court of Appeal decided by a majority that it was payable by the Board.

[5] Cf. below, p. 84. Prices fetched by New River shares, and fractions of them, and amounts paid in dividends, at various dates, may be found in W. Duncombe Pink,

Sir Hugh himself did not long survive the new arrangement with Charles I. He was already an old and sick man; less than a week after the conclusion of the bargain with the King he made his will, and on 7 December 1631 he died. The £3,000 lent him in 1614 by the City of London was still owing, and after 'considerable hesitation', we read, 'the Court of Aldermen instructed the City Sheriff to recover the money by suing on Myddelton's bond'.[1] Lady Myddelton had authority by his will to dispose of a number of her husband's assets in order to pay his debts, but she was evidently in difficulties for some time. His property in the Welsh mines, for example, cannot have been readily disposable; in fact they became derelict, and it was not until 1636 that she found someone prepared to take a lease of them.[2] So far from being able to repay the city's £3,000, she was obliged 'to seek satisfaction from the city for losses sustained by his estate' on account of 'many breaches made in the pipes of water and otherwise upon occasion of divers great fires'. The Common Council had this question under consideration for nearly two years; at length, on 2 October 1634, they agreed to raise £1,000 for her 'by assessment on the wards', but they were in doubt whether to hand it over to her for her own use, or only as executrix of her late husband's will, 'to be distributed according to the custom of this Citty, whereof he died a Freeman'. They stipulated that the city should be allowed to fix cocks, or hydrants, in the mains in each ward, from which water could be drawn in cases of fire, instead of cutting the pipes, as had been the practice on previous occasions. By 1635 Myddelton's loan was still outstanding, and the £1,000 that his widow had been promised had not yet been raised. On 12 May in that year she petitioned the Court of Aldermen to allow this £1,000 to be set off in part satisfaction of Sir Hugh's debt, promising that she would endeavour to discharge the remainder forthwith, and the Court agreed to this.[3]

Notes on the Middleton Family (1891), p. 37; T. Pennant, *London* (1806), p. 78; J. Nelson, *History and Antiquities of the Parish of Islington* (1823), p. 166; S. Lewis, *History and Topography of . . . Islington* (1842), p. 428; W. J. Pinks, *History of Clerkenwell* (1865), p. 459. Cf. also W. R. Scott, *Joint Stock Companies* (Cambridge, 1911), iii. 31.

[1] R. R. Sharpe, *London and the Kingdom* (1894), ii. 26.

[2] Cf. below, p. 128.   [3] R. R. Sharpe, op. cit. ii. 27.

From now on the New River Company's affairs became more prosperous. The population of London was increasing, and the dividend on an Adventurers' share, which had been only about £14 in 1635, had risen to £33 in 1640. By 1680 it was £145; by 1700 over £200. For some years in the eighteenth century the company seems to have had some difficulty in holding the position it had attained; then in the early nineteenth century, after another advance, there was a sharp falling off in profits, due partly to ruinous competition, and partly to the heavy expenditure involved in replacing the old wooden mains by cast iron pipes. A turning point was reached in 1817, when the companies north of the Thames made an agreement together; then, when the London Bridge Waterworks came to an end in 1822, shortly before the demolition of the old bridge, its property was bought by the New River Company. During the rest of the nineteenth century the company went ahead at an unprecedented rate, and in 1897 an Adventurers' share fetched over £125,000.[1] By the Metropolis Water Act of 1902 the New River Company's undertaking passed under the control of the Metropolitan Water Board, but the present New River Company Ltd. administers the old company's landed estates, which did not pass to the Board.

Two-thirds of London's water-supply now comes from the Thames, but the New River still brings some of the remainder, though no longer from the original Chadwell and Amwell springs. The spring at Amwell has been completely dry for very many years, and in the summer of 1898 the Chadwell spring, which had previously shown signs of failure in dry summers, also ceased to flow.[2] It was then pumped quite dry and the mud cleared out, and towards the autumn it gradually resumed its former flow. In the following summer, however, it dried up again, and nowadays it is only after wet weather that it produces any

---

[1] Some statistics about the company in the second half of the nineteenth century are given at the end of an article by W. F. Andrews on 'Chadwell Spring' in *East Herts Arch. Soc. Trans.* i (1899), pp. 7–14.

[2] Londoners could hardly believe that the spring had dried up, and the report that it had done so was officially denied, but 'the fact remained that it had ceased to flow, and did not yield any water for some time' (ibid.).

water. It can hardly be doubted that the main reason for this was the lowering of the plane of saturation in the chalk of the whole area, for which the erection of pumping-stations by the New River Company at various wells in the district was largely responsible.[1] Today most of the water in the New River comes from the Lea, by the cut above Ware which was originally only intended to supplement it.

In its original winding course the New River was more than forty miles long, but by means of aqueducts, embankments, and tunnels its course has since been considerably shortened,[2] though in some places (in the public park at Enfield, for example) parts of the original loops have been left as ornamental waters. In 1946 it ceased to flow to New River Head, and it now terminates at the filtering and pumping plant at Green Lanes, Stoke Newington. The Round Pond, which was given up in 1914, has become a concrete yard, and the total length of the river is now only about twenty-four miles. In its course through the suburbs it is nowadays closely fenced in, but in the open country nearer its source it still presents an appearance that probably differs little from what it was in Myddelton's day. In places it has been widened somewhat, but its depth, seldom exceeding five feet, is much the same as it always was.[3] A number of alterations, including the removal of the Highbury and Bush Hill frames, were carried out by Robert Mylne, the architect of Blackfriars Bridge, who was engineer to the company in the later years of the eighteenth century. One of the pleasantest spots on the river is at the foot of the slope below Great Amwell church, where, on an island planted with weeping willows and a yew tree, Mylne erected a monument, consisting of an urn standing on a square pedestal of Portland stone, with inscriptions commemorating Myddelton's achievement.

1 Ibid., and *V.C.H. Herts.* i (1902), p. 57. In its prime the Chadwell spring was estimated to yield about 4,000,000 gallons a day. A lively description of the Chadwell and Amwell springs, as they were before the New River was made, was contributed by the vicar of Amwell, the Rev. Thomas Hassall, to Edmund Howes's *Continuation of John Stow's Annales or a Generall Chronicle of England* (1631), p. 1015.

2 A survey made in 1723, by which date about two miles of loops had been cut out, gave the length as a little over 38¾ miles (W. Maitland, *History of London* (1739), p. 630).

3 *Journal of the Instn. of Civil Engineers*, vol. 31 (1948), p. 12.

The impressions made by his achievement on people's minds have varied considerably. To contemporaries, such as Stow's continuator, Anthony Munday, it seemed astonishing. In the eighteenth century it inspired two poems, neither of sufficient merit to deserve extensive repetition (though one is markedly inferior to the other), but interesting for the divergence in their attitude. In one, 'New River, a Poem', by William Garbott,[1] 'immortal Middleton' is hailed as the glory of his age, and his peaceful achievements are contrasted with 'destructive wars'. The poem proceeds, in doggerel verses, to describe the sources of the river and its construction with James I's assistance, enumerates the bridges over it, 'the most of Timber, some of Brick, some Stone', and its course:

> Through Cheshunt Park and Theobalds he glides;
> Through both the Enfield Parks he gently slides;

till at length the river reaches Islington, and the pageant of the opening ceremony is described. In a final comparison with the 'Aquaeducts of Rome' the New River is declared to be by far the nobler achievement, because its water is taken into people's houses 'by pipes of lead', and 'of those at Rome the like cannot be said'.

The writer of the other poem, John Scott of Amwell, may quite possibly have had this effusion in mind when in 1766 he published his 'Amwell, a Descriptive Poem'. In this he refers scornfully to the work of 'the Cambrian artist':

> ... suppos'd a work
> Of matchless skill, by those who ne'er had heard
> How from Preneste's heights and Anio's banks
> By Tivoli to Rome's imperial walls
> On marble arches came the limpid store. . . .

In contrast with these Miltonic splendours of a Roman aqueduct

> ... our mercenary stream
> No grandeur boasting, here obscurely glides
> O'er grassy lawns or under willow shades. . . .

---

[1] Undated, but from internal evidence (it mentions three rival undertakings as 'up-starts') apparently written in the early eighteenth century.

while

> old Lee . . . surveys
> With eye indignant his diminished tide.[1]

If the New River must be compared with a Roman aqueduct, to which it bears little resemblance, there is more to be said for Scott's opinion than for Garbott's, and some writers have undoubtedly exaggerated the magnitude and the difficulty, as they also exaggerated the cost, of Myddelton's task. But we need not therefore belittle it, or the benefits it brought to Londoners. If the physical obstacles were comparatively insignificant, human opposition was formidable, and in the face of this, as well as daunting financial anxiety, it needed unusual fortitude and determination to persevere, and in the end to succeed.

[1] Yet another poem, *Apostrophe to the New River*, by A. Heraud, beginning 'Stream of the Cambrian artist! hail, all hail . . .', appeared in the *Gentleman's Magazine* for 1821 (xci, part 2, pp. 65–67). It is reprinted in W. J. Pinks, *History of Clerkenwell* (1865), p. 468.

VI

BRADING HARBOUR

In the early seventeenth century there were numerous schemes for the reclamation of fens and marshes. The Dutch, much of whose country had been gained from the waters, were regarded as the experts in work of this kind, and about 1621 Cornelius Vermuyden was invited to England to deal with a breach in the embankment of the Thames near Dagenham in Essex. Later he went on to reclaim Hatfield Chase and adjacent areas in the neighbourhood of the Isle of Axholme, on the borders of Yorkshire and Lincolnshire. Vermuyden and other Dutch engineers were also engaged in the draining of large areas in the Fens, not without considerable opposition from the Fenmen, who feared that their traditional occupations of fishing and wildfowling would be injured. Oliver Cromwell's championship of the Fenmen is a well-known episode in his early career.

One of the areas reclaimed about this time, though with only brief success, was Brading Harbour, at the eastern end of the Isle of Wight. Apart from the small inlet near Bembridge, still marked on the Ordnance maps as Brading Harbour, this is nowadays a tract of flat alluvial land, but in the early seventeenth century most of it was covered with sea-water at high tide. In his *Lives of the Engineers* Samuel Smiles printed a full-page 'View of Brading Haven, temporarily reclaimed by Sir Hugh Myddelton, as seen from the village of Brading', and described its appearance in his day. 'At low water it appears a wide mud flat, through the middle of which a small stream, called the Yar, winds its way from near the village of Brading, at the head of the haven, to the sea at its eastern extremity; whilst at high tide it forms a beautiful and apparently inland lake, embayed between hills of moderate elevation covered with trees, in many places down to the water's edge.' The entrance from the sea, between Bembridge Point and the spit of sand called the Duver, near St. Helen's, was so narrow that from most points of view the haven seemed to be completely landlocked.

Parts of the edges of this tract, originally some 850 acres in extent, had been reclaimed before Myddelton's time. Sir William Russell, the Warden of the Isle of Wight in Edward I's reign, had taken in a piece near the head of the haven, building Yarbridge and a causeway over the marsh to his manor of Yaverland. Before this, the salt water reached as far as Sandown, making Yaverland and Bembridge virtually an island, but at some early period the whole area must have been above sea level, for Sir John Oglander records that after Myddelton had reclaimed it a well lined with stone was found almost in the middle, 'which argueth it had been firm land and inhabited'. Then in 1562 George Oglander of Nunwell and German Richards of Yaverland successfully gained the North Marsh and some adjoining lands, and in 1594 Edward Richards of Yaverland took in Mill Marsh and other meadows between Yarbridge and the sluice about a mile downstream from there.[1] King James I was interested in land reclamation, and in 1616 a certain Henry Gibb, who was a groom of the King's bedchamber, asked and obtained 'for the benefit of his father, John Gibb', a grant of 'lands called Brading . . . which have been much overflowed by the sea, and are to be inclosed at his expense'.[2] According to Sir John Oglander (who says John Gibb 'begged it' of the King), he was 'the man that King James trusted to carry the reprieve to Winchester for my Lord George Cobham and Sir Walter Raleigh when they were on the scaffold to be executed'.[3] Oglander further records that 'this Gibb was put on to beg it of King James by Sir Bevis Thelwall, who was then one of the pages of the bedchamber'.[4] He in turn sought the co-operation of Hugh Myddelton.

[1] The chief source of information about the reclamation of Brading Harbour is the memoirs of Sir John Oglander of Nunwell (1585–1655), printed in *The Oglander Memoirs* (ed. W. H. Long, Newport, I.W., 1888), pp. 110 ff. I have quoted extensively from this in the following pages, modernizing the spelling.

[2] *Cal. S.P.D. 1611–18*, p. 381.

[3] This was at the beginning of James I's reign, in 1603, when they had been accused of being implicated in a Catholic plot against the King.

[4] In *Cal. S.P.D. 1619–23*, p. 414, Thelwall is described as 'Clerk of the Great Wardrobe'.

Thelwall, like Myddelton, was a Welshman who had gone up to London to make a career. The Myddelton and Thelwall families were neighbours in Denbighshire, and had had personal and financial contacts for some years before Hugh Myddelton and Bevis Thelwall became partners. Thus on 27 September 1609 Sir John Salusbury (a member of another prominent family in that part of Wales) wrote to Hugh's elder brother Thomas Myddelton, at Chirk Castle, about some money owing to Eubule Thelwall, which Thelwall wanted to have repaid, and asked him to approach Hugh and Robert Myddelton in case they could help by advancing money to Thelwall.[1] Eubule Thelwall later became Principal of Jesus College, Oxford; Bevis, who was his youngest brother, was bound apprentice to a mercer in Cheapside, married his master's daughter, and went into partnership with his father-in-law. On the accession of James I, with whom he became friendly, he gave up the silk trade and obtained a position in the royal bedchamber.[2] Sir John Oglander's portrait of him is not particularly flattering. He calls him 'a broken citizen', and 'a very bold fellow, and one that King James very well affected'. He also had his wits about him. He was 'an understanding man, and knowing how to handle the Scots' he gained 'a fair estate' for himself 'by getting the Scots to beg for themselves that which he first found out for them, and then himself buying of them with ready money under half the value'. Over the Brading scheme he seems to have gone even further, for having apparently agreed to purchase the grant of the haven from Gibb, he then refused to pay him anything, because some of the 'gentlemen of the Island', who owned the adjacent land, contested the grant, claiming that the haven belonged to them. The case was heard in the Court of Exchequer, and 'King James was wonderful earnest in the business, because it concerned his old servant, and also because it would be a leading case for the fens in Lincolnshire'. Judgement was given against the landowners, but according to Oglander Thelwall still refused to pay anything 'till he could see that it was feasible to be inned from the sea', and even when the work

---

[1] *Cal. Salusbury Correspondence, 1553–c. 1700* (Cardiff, 1954), p. 96.
[2] See *Dictionary of Welsh Biography*, s.v. 'Thelwall'.

had been finished it was only under compulsion from the King that he and Myddelton gave John Gibb, 'whom the king called Father', £2,000.

Sir John Oglander, however, while an accurate observer and reporter of what came under his personal observation, is not always so trustworthy on other matters, and his version of these financial transactions appears to be somewhat confused. In fact he gives two versions of them, in one of which he says that Gibb sold his grant to Myddelton and Thelwall for £1,000. According to the footnote in Samuel Smiles's first edition,[1] the original grant to Gibb was cancelled, and on 30 June 1622 the King granted the haven to Hugh Myddelton, Robert Bateman, Citizen and Skinner of London, and Richard Myddelton, Citizen and Grocer. Hugh Myddelton was to pay the King £1,000 down and two half-yearly payments of £500 at Lady Day and Michaelmas 1622; the King would pass on the £1,000 and the bonds for the two sums of £500 to Gibb. Now both Bateman and Richard Myddelton (son of Hugh's eldest brother Richard) were among the original 'adventurers' in the New River Company, and it is not at all unlikely that they were also partners with Hugh Myddelton in the Brading scheme. Thelwall's name does not appear at all in this grant, and it would appear that, while he initiated Gibb's original approach to the King, he at first took no active part in the undertaking, and possibly Myddelton decided to step in and buy the rights from Gibb when Thelwall was refusing to pay. Later Thelwall became a partner, and in 1624 he bought out Myddelton's interest.

However that may be, it is clear that the original grant to Gibb was followed by disputes and recriminations, and there was a delay of four years before work began. A letter to the Solicitor-General dated 13 August 1620[2] refers to 'the composition to be made by him with Hugh Middleton, touching the draining of certain lands in the Isle of Wight', and at length, when arrangements

---

[1] *Lives of the Engineers*, i (1861), p. 137. He gave no reference, and omitted the footnote in the second edition, but there seems no reason to doubt its accuracy, except for the dates. If the first £1,000 was to be paid when the grant was made (30 June 1622), the two payments of £500 were presumably to be made at Michaelmas 1622 and Lady Day 1623. [2] *Cal. S.P.D. 1619–23*, p. 172.

had been completed, Dutch workmen[1] were brought over for the work, and 'they began to inn the haven about the 20th of December, 1620'. Wooden piles were driven and an embankment made across the narrowest part of the entrance to the haven, opposite Bembridge, and Samuel Smiles records that 'the black piles driven into the bottom of the haven are still to be seen sticking up at low water; and only a few years since the old gates which served for a sluice were dug up near the Boat Houses'.[2] Myddelton was granted a patent or 'special privilege' to have the sole use for fourteen years of 'a new invencōn or way for the wyninge and drayninge of anie grounds overflowen with water', which 'he hath (by his great paynes and charges) devised and found out'.[3] The patent probably referred to the particular mode of construction used by Myddelton in building his embankment, but no details of the invention are given.

Smiles suggested that the main reason for the subsequent collapse of the embankment, as also for the failure of some of Vermuyden's work in the Fens, which had to be corrected by modern engineers, was that the methods in use in the Netherlands were not suited to conditions in England. Undoubtedly Holland and England presented different problems, but Vermuyden was well aware of this. In Holland it was chiefly a question of building dykes to keep out the sea, and banking up the channels of the great rivers, cutting new channels for them where necessary: the polders, even though lying below the water-level, were then drained and kept dry by pumps driven by windmills. The English fenlands, on the other hand, were flooded partly by the rain that fell on them, but mainly by the overflowing of the rivers that traversed them. The main problem was how to provide the rivers with more rapid outfalls to the sea, and there were disputes about the best method of achieving this.[4] At Bembridge part of the

---

[1] Sir John Oglander calls them 'ignorant Dutchmen', who 'put them to an extraordinary charge, at least £2,000 besides the purchase'.

[2] 'The Boat Houses' are on the northern side of the entrance, at the end of the Duver sand-spit opposite Bembridge.

[3] B. Woodcroft (ed.), *Chronological Index of Patents of Invention* (1854), p. 14 (no. 19, dated 2 July 1621).

[4] For an account of Vermuyden's work in Hatfield Chase, the Bedford Level, and

trouble was that the sea tended to choke the outlet with 'sand and
ooze and seaweed', while the volume of water coming down the
stream was not sufficient to scour the channel clear. Apart from
this, however, it seems evident from Sir John Oglander's narra-
tive that the main defect was that the embankment, though built
with 'great stones'[1] and reinforced with piles, rested on a foundation of sand. Consequently, when owing to wet weather and a
spring tide a large volume of fresh water was pent up on one side
of the embankment, while the sea was high on the other side,
'both the waters met underneath in the loose sand', and the embankment was undermined.

A contributory cause of its collapse may have been failure to
maintain it properly, but for some years the bank held, though
we gather that from an agricultural point of view the scheme
was a disappointment. Nearly half the area reclaimed, Sir John
Oglander records, was 'a light running sand, and of little worth.
The best of it was down at the further end next to Brading, my
marsh, and Knight's Tenement in Bembridge'. He reckoned that
of the 706 acres reclaimed, 200 acres might be worth 6s. 8d. an
acre, the rest being worth only 2s. 6d. an acre. Myddelton 'tried
all experiments in it: he sowed wheat, barley, oats, cabbage seed,
and last of all rape seed, which proved best; but all the others
came to nothing'. He, or Thelwall after him, also built a 'barn
and dwelling-house, and water-mill', which, 'with the ditching and
quick-setting, and making all the partitions', must have cost, Sir
John thought, not less than £200. The initial cost of the reclamation he put at £4,000, and he reckoned that with this, and
the £2,000 paid to Gibb, the total expenditure from the time work
began until the bank gave way was £7,000.[2] The loss, however,
fell on Thelwall, for Myddelton, whether from disappointment
with the poor quality of the reclaimed land, or a desire to concen-
trate on his Welsh mines, sold his interest to Thelwall in September 1624. Myddelton thus ('like a crafty fox and subtle citizen',

elsewhere, and a discussion of the different problems involved and the disputes that arose
out of them, see L. E. Harris, *Vermuyden and the Fens* (1953).

[1] See Myddelton's letter to Sir John Wynn of Gwydir, quoted below, p. 98.
[2] Thelwall and Myddelton themselves later declared that they had spent £8,000
(*Acts P.C., June–Dec. 1626*, p. 96).

says Oglander) presumably recovered his capital outlay, or at any rate a substantial part of it.

Sir John Oglander had approved of the scheme, but, as happened also in the Fens, local people were generally opposed to it, 'thinking by a little fishing and fowling there would accrue more benefit than by pasturage'. Sir John felt sure that 'it caused, after the first three years, a great deal more health in these parts than was ever before'. Remarkably enough, it had the opposite effect on farm animals, for 'whereas we thought it would have improved our marshes, certainly they were the worse for it, and rotted sheep which before fatted there'. Some local inhabitants even complained to the Government that the scheme threatened the security of the island, 'for that thereby an enemy may have faire and easie landing upon that parte of the Island which he had not before'. Myddelton and Thelwall scouted such a suggestion, which certainly sounds rather absurd, pointing out 'that there are divers spacious landing places besides adjacent to the said peece of ground by them taken in where an enemy may with lyke ease and comoditie (if not with more) land his forces'. One would have thought that such a complaint was hardly worth serious attention, but on 18 July 1626 the Privy Council directed Sir John Ogle to pay a visit of inspection, taking with him 'Bernard Johnson, ingineire', and after interviewing 'such persons of the said Isle for informacion only as you shall fynd cause', and personally taking 'an exact viewe of that peece of ground complayned of as alsoe of the said other places adjoyning upon that coast', to 'make a certificate in writing to this Board, to the end such further order may be taken as may best stand with the safetie of the Island and the preservation of the right and inheritance of the said parties'.[1]

Considering that the reclamation had been completed in 1622, four years before this, it is hard to see what action the Privy Council could have taken, unless the complainants were hoping for a demolition order. As it turned out, they had only a few more years to wait, for the end came on 8 March 1630. On this day, Sir John Oglander records:

one Andrew Ripley that was put in to look to Brading Haven by Sir

[1] *Acts P.C., June–Dec. 1626*, p. 96.

Bevis Thelwall came in post to my house in Newport to inform me that the sea had made a breach in the said haven near to the easternmost end. I demanded of him what the charge might be to stop it out; he told me he thought about 40 shillings, whereupon I bid him go thither and get workmen against the next day morning, and some carts, and I would pay them their wages; but the sea the next day came so forcibly in that there was no meddling with it, and Ripley went up presently to London to Sir Bevis Thelwall himself, to have him come down and take some further course; but within four days after the sea had won so much on the haven, and made the breach so wide and deep, that on the 15th of March when I came thither to see it I knewe not well what to judge of it, for whereas at the first £5 would have stopped it out, now I think £200 will not do it, and what will be the event of it time will tell.

Sir Bevis Thelwall himself arrived on 17 March, armed with a letter from Conway, the Secretary of State, to Sir John Oglander and another local magnate, Sir Edward Dennies, 'desiring us to cause my Lady Worsley, on behalf of her son, to make up the breach which happened in her ground through their neglect. She returned us an answer that she thought that the law would not compel her unto it, and therefore she desired to be excused, which answer we returned to my Lord'. Sir John thought it unreasonable that Lady Worsley should have to pay for an accident which would never have happened 'if he had not inned the haven', but Sir Bevis thought 'to recover of her and her son all his charges, which he now sweareth every way to be £2,000'. Sir John declared that he would not wish any friend of his 'to have any hand in the second inning of it'. Even if the bank had not given way when it did, he doubted whether Sir Bevis could have kept the reclaimed land indefinitely; he believed that the outlet would inevitably have become choked in time, and then the haven would have been inundated once more, so that 'in my opinion it is not good meddling with a haven so near the main ocean'. Nevertheless, he tells us, 'all the better sort of the Island were very sorry for Sir Bevis Thelwall, and the commoner sort were as glad as to say truly of Sir Bevis that he did the country many good offices, and was ready at all times to do his best for the public and everyone'.

The upshot of all this was a series of lawsuits, appeals, and inquiries, including 'a great suit in the Chancery' between Thelwall and Myddelton, who for some time had been partners in the Welsh mines. Their partnership, however, was in any case near its end, for Sir Hugh died in 1631. Thelwall evidently failed to compel Lady Worsley to make good the damage, and the haven remained an inlet of the sea for over 200 years. In 1699 Sir Robert Worsley must have been considering the possibility of a fresh reclamation, for he had an estimate made, according to which the cost would have been £4,170, including £1,000 'profit or recompense to the undertakers'.[1] Nothing was done, however, until at last, in 1874, it was proposed to build a branch railway line from Bembridge to join the Isle of Wight company's line at Brading. To carry out this scheme, in which the subsequently notorious Jabez Balfour was concerned,[2] a company called the Brading Harbour Improvement and Railway Company was incorporated, with powers to make an embankment between Bembridge and St. Helen's. The northern end of this is about half a mile further inland than Myddelton's embankment, and it is considerably longer than his—about a mile long altogether—and more substantial, carrying a roadway, with the railway line roughly parallel to it on the landward side. The railway was opened in May 1882, and the effect was to reclaim a considerable portion of the harbour, leaving only the small inlet that now exists open to the sea. These works, however, proved unsatisfactory, difficulty being caused, as in Sir John Oglander's time, by the accumulation of silt, which threatened to block the harbour. Accordingly further powers were obtained in 1896, defining the limits of the harbour, and permitting the company to improve the access to it by dredging.[3] The railway line is now disused, but the embankment and the road still keep back the tide.

By an odd coincidence, there was to be a second, and unhappier,

---

[1] R. Worsley, *History of the Isle of Wight* (1781), p. 197.

[2] *V.C.H. Hants and Isle of Wight*, v (1912), p. 157. Jabez Balfour's fraudulent handling of the funds of the Liberator Building Society, which went bankrupt in 1892, led to his flight to Argentina and subsequent extradition and imprisonment. See R. H. Gretton, *A Modern History of the English People* (one vol. edn., 1930), pp. 322, 326, 370.

[3] C. F. Dendy Marshall, *History of the Southern Railway* (1936), pp. 247–8.

contact between the families of Myddelton and Oglander. The first Sir Hugh had stayed at Nunwell, the ancestral home of the Oglander family, while supervising the reclamation work. In 1677 his grandson Sir Hugh Myddelton (not the third baronet, but a son of the first Sir Hugh's seventh son Simon, created a baronet as Sir Hugh Myddelton of Hackney) married Dorothea Oglander, Sir John's granddaughter. The bridegroom, we are told, was 'apparently well to do as well as charming', but he was in fact a spendthrift, who made his wife's life 'a veritable nightmare'. She 'eventually obtained a separation from her husband and particularly directed in her will that her epitaph should describe her as "the unhappy wife" of Sir Hugh Myddelton'. She died in 1701 at the age of 45, but 'this parting shot from the grave was disallowed by her executors', and her tombstone, in Long Melford church, Suffolk, calls her simply 'wife of Sir Hugh Myddelton, Bart.'[1]

Hearing of Myddelton's achievement at Brading Harbour,[2] Sir John Wynn of Gwydir conceived the idea of inviting him to undertake the reclamation of the expanses of sand, called Traeth Mawr and Traeth Bychan, which lay between Aberglaslyn and the sea, in North Wales. Addressing Sir Hugh as 'Right worthie Sir, my good cousin, and one of the great honors of the nation', he declared that he would say 'what the Jewes said to Christ— We have heard of thy greate workes done abroade, doe somewhat in thine own countrey'. He went on to describe the 'two washes', which entered the sea 'by one issue, which is not a mile broad at full sea, and verie shallow', and remarked that 'the fresh currents that run into the sea are both vehement and greate, and carie with them much sand; besides the southerly wind [which] usually bloweth fulle into the haven's mouth, carrieth with it so much sand, that it hath overwhelmed a great quantitie of the ground adjacent'. Close at hand and 'to be had at a very cheap rate' were 'abundance of wood, brush, and other materialls fit to make mounds', which he believed were used 'in Lincolnshire, to

---

[1] C. Aspinall-Oglander, *Nunwell Symphony* (1945), p. 140.

[2] Rumour evidently magnified the extent of the achievement. Instead of the actual 700-odd acres, Wynn had heard that he had gained 2,000 acres from the sea. His letter to Myddelton is dated 1 Sept. 1625.

expell the sea'. He had always wanted 'to further my country in such actions as might be for their profit, and leave a remembrance of my endeavors', but being inexperienced in such matters and hindered by other business he had 'only wished well and done nothing'. Sir Hugh at this time was working his mines and living at Lodge, between Machynlleth and Aberystwyth, and being thus 'not above a daies journey' away, Wynn urged him to 'take a ride' and come to see the place, offering 'to adventure a brace of hundred pounds to joyne with you in the worke' if Sir Hugh thought the undertaking feasible. 'I have leade ore on my grounds great store', he added, 'and other minerals near my house', which lay only another day's journey farther on, and Sir Hugh would be 'most kindly wellcome' if he would pay a visit there. 'If I did knowe the day certaine when you would come to visit Traeth Mawr', he concluded, 'my son Owen Wynn shall attend you there, and conduct you thence to my house'.

Sir Hugh replied the next day declining the offer. Although his letter had been printed more than once, so little has survived from his pen that it is worth reproducing again:[1]

Honorable Sir,

I have received your kind letter. Few are the things done by me, for which I give God the glory. It may please you to understand my first undertaking of publick works was amongst my owne, within less than a myle of the place where I hadd my first being, 24 or 25 years since, in seekinge of coales for the town of Denbigh.

Touchinge the drowned lands near your lyvinge, there are many things considerable therein. Iff to be gayned, which will hardlie be performed without great stones, which was plentifull at the Weight [i.e. the Isle of Wight], as well as wood; and great sums of money to be spent, not hundreds, but thousands—and first of all his Majesty's interest must be got. As for myself, I am grown into years, and full of busines here at the mynes, the river at London, and other places— my weeklie charge being above £200; which maketh me verie unwillinge to undertake anie other worke: and the least of theis, whether

[1] Wynn's letter and Myddelton's reply are nos. 1366 and 1367 in *Cal. Wynn Papers* (N.L.W.). Both are printed in T. Pennant, *Tours in Wales* (1784), ii. 185–7, and in *History of the Gwydir Family* (1878), pp. vii–viii. Samuel Smiles printed the reply in the section on Myddelton in his *Lives of the Engineers*.

the drowned lands or mynes, requireth a whole man, with a large purse. Noble Sir, my desire is great to see you, which should draw me a farr longer waie; yet such are my occasions at this tyme here, for the settling of this great worke, that I can hardlie be spared one howre in a daie. My wieff being also here, I cannot leave her in a strange place. Yet my love to publique works, and desire to see you (if God permit) maie another tyme drawe me into those parts. Soe with my heartie com̄en-dations I com̄itt you and all your good desires to God.

Your assured lovinge couzin to command,
Hugh Myddelton

Lodge, Sept. 2nd. 1625.

Though nothing was done in Sir John Wynn's time, the recla-mation of Traeth Mawr was ultimately achieved, early in the nineteenth century, by William Alexander Madocks, an indus-trialist and radical politician, who apparently wished to emulate the great pioneers and inventors of the past, and had read about Sir John Wynn in Pennant's *Tours*. During the last thirty years of the eighteenth century landowners in the neighbourhood had already reclaimed a number of small areas on the fringes of the estuary by building earth banks, but Madocks embarked on a more ambitious plan. Having inherited a fortune from his father, he bought the estate of Tan-yr-allt in 1798, and shortly afterwards enclosed 1,000 acres on the west side of the estuary, where he built the town of Tremadoc to perpetuate his name. Then in 1807 he obtained an Act of Parliament for the reclamation of the rest of the Traeth. An embankment a mile long, carrying a road (and later the Ffestiniog Railway) was made from the Merioneth shore to the town of Portmadoc, which was built on the Caernarvon-shire side. Richard Fenton, who visited Tremadoc in August 1810, described 'the new embankment' as 'a gigantick undertaking . . . which would have appalled any other genius than that of the Gentleman to whose enterprising spirit we owe it'.

Early in 1812, however, less than a year after its completion, the sea broke through in a storm, and the work had to be done over again. When Fenton paid a second visit at the beginning of August 1813, 'to see the patriotick work at this place', the flood-gates seemed to him 'to be well constructed and do their duty well. But alas! the principal work, the Embankment, appeared in several parts in a state of great decadence, and for one third of it, letting in the Sea like a Cullender, which then, at its full, was assailing its sides most violently, as it were impatient to recover its former Empire, which if not strenuously opposed in time, I fear it will.'[1] Fenton anticipated 'the probable failure of this great plan', but in fact a concerted effort was made to repair the damage. Hundreds of local farmers helped in carting materials, and the poet Shelley, who had leased Tan-yr-allt, gave enthusiastic support.[2] The work of reconstruction was completed by the end of September 1814, with the result that some 3,000 acres were reclaimed from the sea. Madocks had had visions of Portmadoc becoming the terminal for cross-channel traffic to Ireland, but these hopes were never realized, though for a time it enjoyed some prosperity from the export of slates. Tremadoc, however, declined into a village, and, as at Brading Harbour, the quality of the reclaimed land proved disappointing; but at any rate the embankment resulted in a much needed improvement in communications.[3]

[1] Richard Fenton, *Tours in Wales, 1804–13* (ed. John Fisher, Cambrian Archaeol. Assoc. supplemental volume, 1917), pp. 224, 233, 234.

[2] E. Dowden, *Life of Percy Bysshe Shelley* (1932), pp. 153–5.

[3] See *Dictionary of Welsh Biography*, s.v. 'Madocks', and F. J. North, B. Campbell, and R. Scott, *Snowdonia* (The New Naturalist, 1949), pp. 387–8. Smiles in a footnote gives a considerably larger acreage. The Ffestiniog Railway, since abandoned and recently resurrected for part of its length by railway enthusiasts, was not actually completed until after Madocks's death.

VII

THE MINES ROYAL IN WALES

ON Cornelius Johnson's portrait of Sir Hugh Myddelton appear the words *Fontes Fodinae*, in allusion to his two principal achievements—bringing water to London and working silver mines in Wales. Among many frequently repeated errors is the idea that he financed the New River with the profits from his mines—a misapprehension probably derived from Sir John Pettus, who declared that had he not done so 'certainly he would have been Master of a Mass of Wealth', and concluded sententiously that 'great Wits and Purses seldom know how to give bounds to their Designments, and by undertaking too many things, fail in all'.[1] This may be true in general, but was less than fair to Myddelton, and in any case was beside the mark, for the New River had been completed before he first took a lease of the Welsh mines. It is true, however, that his mining profits helped to extinguish the losses he had incurred on account of the New River, and that had he not been embarrassed in this way he would in all probability have died a richer man. It is also true that his first mining venture in Wales—an attempt many years previously to find coal in the neighbourhood of his native town of Denbigh[2] had been a failure, but this seems to have been an isolated venture of no great importance.

Most of the Cardiganshire mines, which yielded lead-ore (galena, i.e. lead sulphide) containing variable amounts of silver, are situated in the hills a few miles inland from Aberystwyth, and are thought to have been worked since prehistoric times.[3] Pettus and others believed, on somewhat dubious evidence,[4] that they

[1] J. Pettus, *Fodinae Regales* (1670), p. 33.   [2] Cf. above, pp. 10, 98.

[3] According to H. J. Fleure, quoted in K. Carpenter, 'Notes on the History of the Cardiganshire Lead Mines', in *Aberystwyth Studies*, v (1923), p. 99.

[4] See W. J. Lewis, 'Some Aspects of Lead Mining in Cardiganshire in the Sixteenth and Seventeenth Centuries', in *Ceredigion* (Journal of the Cardiganshire Antiquarian Soc.), i (1950–1), pp. 177–92. I am indebted to this article for much of the information in the

were worked by the Romans, but, apart from an isolated reference to a lead mine near Llanbadarn in 1305, there appear to be no definite records of mining in Cardiganshire until the reign of Elizabeth I, though the existence of the mines must always have been known. Then, encouraged by government policy, and with the aid of experts brought over from Germany, there was a notable advance in mining, in both extent and technique, in various parts of the kingdom. The company known as the Society of the Mines Royal was incorporated in 1568, with widespread mining rights covering the principality of Wales as well as other areas; but the society was largely occupied at first with copper mines in the Lake District, and it leased its Welsh rights to a series of contractors. The output they achieved seems at first to have been small; but one of them, the London business man Thomas Smyth, commonly known as Customer Smyth, according to Fuller discovered silver at Cwmsymlog,[1] one of the richest of the mines, and worked it in the later years of the sixteenth century with some success, which was reflected in a marked increase in the amount of Welsh silver sent to the Mint. Apart from copper, which was required for ordnance, the main interest in Elizabethan and early Stuart times seems to have been in silver, which was badly needed to supply the deficiencies of the coinage; lead from which the silver had been extracted fetched only a low price, partly owing to the competition in European markets of cheap Polish lead,[2] and mines where the ore was poor in silver-content were apt to be abandoned.

Possibly because the cost of transporting the silver to London made its extraction unprofitable, it would appear that lead was often exported before its silver-content had been extracted, as it then commanded a higher price, and it was said that the King of Spain could make a profit of from £2. 10s. to £5 on every ton of

following pages, also to Mr. Lewis's 'The Cwmsymlog Lead Mine', *Ceredigion* ii (1952–5), pp. 27–38. Pettus has an illustration of what in his time were still known as the Roman Works.

[1] T. Fuller, *The History of the Worthies of England* (1662), ed. J. Nichols (1811), ii. 531. Though Smyth got the credit, the work on the spot was directed by a man named Thomas Evans.

[2] According to Maurice Wynn, writing to his father from Hamburg on 31 Aug. 1622: *Cal. Wynn Papers*, no. 1031. Nos. 990 and 1017 also refer to the low price of lead.

British lead by extracting the silver from it.[1] The English Government hoped that when Myddelton took charge of the Welsh mines this practice would cease, and one of the reasons given for encouraging his work was that 'we hold it fit for our honour and necessary for the public good of our realm that the said silver should be separated from the lead . . . for the supply of bullion for our own use, and not exported into foreign parts under colour of the ordinary merchandize of lead, to the enrichment of strangers with our own native commodities'.[2] Customs officers had instructions to stop the export of lead unless special licence had been obtained, and in 1628 'Abraham and Thomas Chamberlaine of London, merchants', complained to the Privy Council that their father had contracted sixteen months previously with Sir Hugh Myddelton to take his whole output of lead, but that the customs officers had made them unload a ship which they had freighted for transport to Holland, and the lead had 'ever since laine on their hands to their great prejudice and disadvantage'. They asked leave to ship it to Holland, together with 150 fother of 'Darbishire lead, for the better sale of the other leade'. Leave was granted, 'provided that the peticioners' quantity of leade of the Royall Mines which they transport, exceed not one hundreth and fifty fother, nor the whole three hundreth Foder'.[3]

At Cwmystwyth, one of the oldest mines in the district, the ore came to the surface 'either as a single lode, or, more probably, as a junction of two or more lodes', in a huge outcrop nearly a mile in length, which was worked as an open quarry.[4] More usually, however, some prospecting or exploration was necessary to locate the veins of ore, and the methods employed for this purpose, as Mr. Lewis has pointed out, were a mixture of superstition and observation. There was a widespread belief, which lasted until well into the nineteenth century, in what were called 'knockers'.

---

[1] Llewelyn Jones, 'The Welsh Mint', in *Economica*, vi (1926), p. 313.

[2] The King to the Council, 9 July, 19 James I, in *Rep. H.M.C.* xiii, pt. 4 (1892), p. 268.

[3] *Acts P.C. July 1628–April 1629*, pp. 63–64. The same volume contains a number of petitions and licences to export lead from various ports to Holland. The Cardiganshire lead was presumably 'poor' desilverized lead. A fother or foder is variously defined as 19½ or 21 cwt.

[4] *The Mines of Cardiganshire, Montgomeryshire and Shropshire*, by Liscombe & Co. (Liverpool, n.d.), s.v. 'Cwmystwyth'.

A knocker was 'some Being', or spirit, 'that Inhabits in the Con-
caves and Hollows of the Earth; and . . . it is . . . kind to some
Men of suitable Tempers, and directs them to the Ore by . . .
knocking'.[1] The divining-rod was often used in prospecting for
ore, but there were also well-known surface indications of the
likely presence of mineral veins—sparse or poor vegetation,
flowers paler than their normal shade, or the occurrence of rocks
and stones of particular colours. The discovery of ore, however,
was often a matter of chance. It might be revealed by the fall of a
tree, or a landslide, or when the soil was washed away by a rain-
storm, or even by ploughing.

Another common superstition led miners to fill in old workings in the belief that the ore would grow again and provide a
fresh 'crop' in the future. This was a very ancient belief, on the
strength of which tithes had been payable on minerals in the middle
ages. In the seventeenth century Sir Edward Coke denied this,
and quoted recent judgements to show that 'tithes shall not be
payd of anything that is of the substance of the earth and are [sic]
not annuall, as of quarries of stone, turfe, flagges, tynne, lead,
brick, tyle, marle, coales, chalk, pots of earth, and the like'.[2]
Mr. Christopher Hill points out, however, that in these judgements, which 'flatly contradicted medieval practice', the common
lawyers were changing the law, and ecclesiastical lawyers still
tried to maintain that tithe was due on stone, turfs, and minerals
because they 'renew themselves when extracted'. He adds that
tithes were paid by custom on tin in Devon and Cornwall and on
lead in Derbyshire, 'but there were struggles over such tithes',
and he comments that these beliefs 'were more likely to be held
by clerical academics than by miners, and they soon became old-
fashioned in England, though they survived in less industrially
developed countries like France.' It seems, however, that the
miners were less scientific in this respect than the common
lawyers, and even in Sweden, a country where mining was extensively developed, and as late as the eighteenth century, Lin-
naeus believed that minerals grew.[3]

[1] W. Hooson, *The Miner's Dictionary* (Wrexham, 1747), s.v. 'Knocker'.
[2] Coke, 2 *Inst.* 651.
[3] J. E. C. Hill, *Economic Problems of the Church* (Oxford, 1956), pp. 84, 85.

When a vein of ore had been located, the usual practice in early times was to open it up by digging a trench along its course, and in the sixteenth and early seventeenth centuries most of the mining was still carried out by opencast trenches, called rakes, rather than by deep shafts. This was partly because of a belief that ore from deeper levels was of poorer quality,[1] and partly too because of the lack of adequate tools for excavating underground, but largely because of the difficulty of draining and ventilating deep mines. Water was a serious problem even with open trenches, though much would depend on the lie of the land, and in certain situations deeper workings were possible. At Cwmsymlog, which is low-lying, the workings were said to become flooded 'before they could get above eight or ten yards deep; though in some other high grounds they have gone fifty yards'.[2] It might be possible to dig a trench in such a way that the water would run out at either or both ends, but more often a trench would become deeper as it followed the lode, so that 'dead' water would collect in the bottom. One way of dealing with this was to divide the trench into sections by building dams across it at intervals; then the water would be thrown out of the working section into exhausted sections with hollow wooden shovels. In a small working the water might be got rid of in buckets hauled up by ropes. Sometimes, when an outcrop occurred at the foot of a slope, water might be a help rather than a hindrance. A store of water was collected above the spot to be worked, and then suddenly released down a prepared channel, so as to wash away the overlying soil; but this process, called 'hushing', though long practised, was not well thought of, presumably because it might wash away the ore as well as the overburden. Trenches often had steps at one end, or, if the workings were wide and deep, wooden ladders were used for access. In narrow trenches, wooden struts, called stemples, were wedged in across them, serving both to shore up the sides and also as

[1] A belief not without foundation, apparently, for according to R. F. Tylecote, *Metallurgy in Archaeology* (1962), p. 74, 'the silver content of lead ores is generally higher in the upper layers of a deposit, probably owing to concentration by dissolution of the lead'.

[2] Lewis Morris, *An Account of the Lead and Silver Mines in the King's Mannor called Cwmmwd y Perveth* . . . (N.L.W. Add. MS. 603 E), p. 33. This was written in 1744.

steps. The sides of shafts were similarly supported, and in the deeper mines we read of the erection of 'stages one above another' for men to stand on when working.[1]

When the vein had been opened up, the ore was extracted by hammer and wedge. For this purpose the earliest miners used 'water-worn pebbles, of about the length and breadth of a man's hand and three inches thick, probably held in a twisted stick', of which quantities were found by later generations of miners in the old workings.[2] If the rock was too hard, fires were lit and left burning for some hours; water was then thrown on the rock while it was still hot, causing it to crumble and splinter, so that wedges could be driven in. Although the smoke was a nuisance, fires continued to be used to split the rocks until late in the seventeenth century, when a method of blasting by gunpowder was invented.[3] Before the use of explosives progress was inevitably slow and laborious. From a description of the tools and methods in use at the end of the seventeenth century we gather that by means of 'sharp Chizels, skrew'd to Iron rods, of about four feet long, with which we pounce the Rock into a Powder', it was possible to 'bore a Yard in a Day in a very hard Rock'.[4] When they 'worked downwards with Gad and Sledge [i.e. wedge and hammer] and raised the Oar without a level [i.e. without an adit] by the help of a Water-Engine', it was reckoned that two miners could raise a ton of ore in a week, or forty tons in a year, allowing twelve weeks when the wet made work impossible. Sometimes, however, the output would be less than this, because 'some veins are so small that the Miners cannot raise the Oar without cutting the firm sides along with it', while other veins were 'so troubled with water that three parts of the Time and Labour of the Workmen is spent in keeping the Water, and therefore they can raise but little Oar'.[5]

In shafts, the ore was wound up in buckets with a windlass;

---

[1] (W. Waller), *A Familiar Discourse or Dialogue . . . concerning the Mine-Adventure*, p. 69.

[2] *The Mines of Cardiganshire, Montgomeryshire and Shropshire*, s.v. 'Old Darren'.

[3] News of the use of gunpowder in mining was communicated to the Royal Society in Jan. 1685 (*Phil. Trans.* xv. 354).

[4] (W. Waller), op. cit., p. 52.   [5] Ibid. pp. 67–69.

from opencast workings it was carried in wicker baskets, on the heads or strapped to the backs of men and women. On reaching the surface it was emptied into panniers, which were conveyed by packhorses, each carrying two hundredweight of ore, to the smelting-houses. At first these were scattered in various places, but later, as the timber available for fuel was used up, they came to be concentrated in a few particular spots, near Talybont, Ynyshir, and Garreg. The pig-lead produced was shipped from Garreg, a small port near the head of the Dovey estuary, and according to Mr. Lewis was mostly exported to France and Holland. When silver was extracted from the lead, of which there is no record till the last quarter of the sixteenth century, it had to be sent overland, at considerable expense, to the Mint in London.

Before smelting, the next stage was to wash away the earth, stones, and other impurities in which the ore was embedded, by sieving it in tubs or in troughs known as buddles. In Pettus's inventory of the apparatus in use in 1667 we read of 'three great washing Tubs, two brass wyer Sieves' for ore at Talybont, and 'six tubs, several iron riddles, sieves, buddles, rakes', &c., 'for dressing of oar', at which two 'washers' were employed, at Goginan; also 'several tubs and sieves for dressing of Hillock Oar' at Cwmerfin and Cwmsymlog. At Talybont there were also 'six great Tubs . . ., Buddles, Sieves, Rakes, Shovels and other necessaries for washing and cleansing of Slags'.[1] The dressed ore was broken up, in early days by hand with hammers, but in the seventeenth century with stamps driven by water-power, and then smelted in the smelting-houses with 'black and white coal'. White coal, which was ordinary wood fuel in the form of 'Sticks cut into small Pieces, then slit and dried', was mixed with the black coal (i.e. charcoal), because charcoal by itself gave too fierce a heat. When John Ray visited the silver mills on 6 September 1658 he saw 'two Sorts of Ore, the one rich of Dorrens [Darren] and Consomlogh, the other poorer of Talabont. They mix these, six Parts of Dorrens Ore with Four of Talabont, because Dorrens being rich, will not *melt off the Hearth* without

[1] J. Pettus, *Fodinae Regales*, pp. 36, 37.

such a quantity of the Talabont. Then they carry it in a Barrow from the Store-house, to each Smelter's several Bing'.[1]

Various kinds of smelting furnaces were in use in different parts of the country, some depending on the wind to obtain the necessary draught. In Cardiganshire we read of 'hearths' and 'large smelting bellows' worked by a waterwheel.[2] These hearths seem to have been open furnaces not unlike blacksmiths' forges,[3] in which the ore was thrown directly on the fire; the molten metal then ran out at the bottom into a hollow stone pit lined with clay, called the sump, whence it was ladled out and cast into long bars called sows or pigs. By Myddelton's time experiments were apparently being made with reverberatory furnaces, i.e. closed furnaces in which the ore is not in direct contact with the fuel, but the forced draught causes the flame to strike against the roof, whence it is reverberated back on to the ore. It was probably in furnaces of this type that fuel other than wood-fuel could be used, but they had not yet displaced the older type of open furnace.

Silver was then extracted from the lead in a refining-furnace by the ancient method known as cupellation. The refining-furnace was a closed furnace, covered with a thick, iron-bound stone cap pierced with two holes, in which the bars of lead were suspended lengthwise in iron slings, so that they could be gradually lowered into the furnace as their ends melted. The 'test' or cupel, which lay at the bottom of the refining-furnace, consisted of an oval iron pan, lined a foot thick with a paste made by mixing water with powdered bone-ash. In Pettus's time at Talybont there was a 'large Water-wheel with troughs' which worked 'the annexed Mill to grind Bone-Ashes with a pair of Stones and all things necessary for Grinding and Sifting bone-ashes in order to Refining'.[4] The molten lead was rapidly oxidized, in a draught blown by bellows at the side of the furnace, and converted into litharge, while the silver it contained ran down into the test. The litharge was either absorbed in the bone-ash, or was skimmed or

[1] J. Ray, *Itineraries*, in *Select Remains* (1760), p. 127.
[2] J. Pettus, op. cit., p. 35.
[3] Cf. L. F. Salzman, *English Industries of the Middle Ages* (Oxford, 1923), pp. 55, 56.
[4] J. Pettus, op. cit., p. 36.

blown off the surface of the silver by the bellows. It could be used in making the pigment known as red lead, or it could be converted back into molten lead by a fierce charcoal fire in a reducing furnace. To lessen the wastage of metal, cinders and slag resulting from these processes were collected, and after crushing, sieving, and washing, were smelted over again.

When Myddelton first became interested in the Cardiganshire mines, and obtained a lease from the Society of the Mines Royal, it seems that the metal he, or the Society, had in view was not lead or silver but copper. According to a note preserved among the Sackville manuscripts,[1] his first lease, dated 17 February 1616/17, was to have been for a term of ten years from the following Lady Day, the rent reserved for the copper being £13. 6s. 8d. per annum for the first three years and £20 per annum for the remaining seven years. Three months later, however, Myddelton surrendered this lease and took another, dated 15 May 1617, to run for twenty-one years from the previous Lady Day.[2] This covered 'gold, silver, copper, quicksilver or any other Oares or Mettals whatsoever belonging or appertayning to the priviledge of the . . . Society'; but copper was still the metal expected, for besides a money rental he was to pay 'the moyetie or one halfe of the fifteenth parte of everie hundredth weight' of copper produced, for the first four and a half years to the Society, and for the remainder of the term to the King, but there is no mention of a royalty on other metals.

The lease begins by reciting the 'good opinion' which 'the Governors, Assistants and Society of the Cittie of London of and for the Mines Royal' had of 'Hughe Middleton, Cittizen and Goldsmith of London . . . for that renowned work of his in bringing the new river to the said cittie, and his care and industrie in busines of like nature, tending to the publique good, and confidence in him of the like to be continewed in the Mynes and Mynerall workes . . . to be by these presentes devised'. He is then granted possession of all the mines in Cardiganshire

---

[1] Sackville MS. (now at the office of the Historical MSS. Commission, Quality Court, Chancery Lane), no. 7628a.

[2] Ibid., no. 7628.

belonging to the Society, 'together with all their howses, fornaces, melting howses, refyning howses, tooles and ymplements what-soever to them belongyng or appertayninge within the said Countie'. Myddelton was not to 'sell, alyen or passe over' his entire interests to any person without first obtaining the Society's consent, but he could at any time take on a partner or partners,[1] or surrender the lease on giving six months notice. It has been pointed out that by the seventeenth century the Mines Royal Society had practically ceased active mining operations on its own account, and confined itself to drawing a revenue from lessees to whom it granted licences to exercise its mining rights,[2] but it seems that within a few years even the issue of leases was taken over by the Crown, and for some time the Society was virtually in abeyance. At any rate, on 21 February 1625, Myddelton obtained from the King a new lease,[3] for thirty-one years free of rent, of the Cardiganshire mines, described as 'formerly granted him by the Governor and Assistants of and for the Mynes Royall'.[4] This new lease, after summarizing the conditions laid down in the previous lease, refers to 'our pleasure signified by our late proclamacōn of the tenth of July last past (1624) con-cerning the Mynes'. This was a proclamation announcing the King's intention to lease the royal mines, except those in Car-diganshire, which were excepted, presumably, because they were to remain Myddelton's preserve. Owners of the land were to have preference in the allocation of mining leases, which were to be for terms of twenty-one years and to carry the conditions of effective working and of paying one tenth of the profits after the first two years.[5]

[1] Sir Bevis Thelwall, who had been associated with Myddelton in the reclamation of Brading Harbour, is mentioned as a partner in 1624 (*Cal. S.P.D. 1623–5*, p. 290).

[2] C. T. Carr, in *Selden Soc.*, vol. 28 (1913), p. xcvi; W. R. Scott, *The Constitution and Finance . . . of Joint Stock Companies* (Cambridge, 1911), ii. 402. Cf. M. B. Donald, *Elizabethan Copper: the History of the Company of Mines Royal, 1568–1605* (1955), pp. 3, 368. Professor Donald attributes the decline of the company to the death of the German technicians with whose help it started operations, and the failure to train any English successors to carry on their work.

[3] S.P.D. James I, 184/120 (*Cal. 1623–5*, p. 480).

[4] S.P.D. James I, 38/13 (*Cal. 1625–6*, p. 535). There seems to have been a delay before the grant became effective, and the lease as finally concluded was dated 30 April 1625.

[5] *Cal. S.P.D. 1623–5*, p. 297.

Now according to Pettus[1] Myddelton paid the Mines Royal Society an annual rent of £400 for his mining rights, and this figure has been repeated by practically every writer on the history of the Cardiganshire mines. Pettus should have known, for he was Deputy-Governor of the Society within a generation of Myddelton's time; but his statement is not borne out by the extant leases, and his brief account of Myddelton's activities is so inaccurate in other respects that one wonders whether it was based on more than gossip, and the wish to fortify the Society's claim to a monopoly of mining rights.[2] The lease dated 15 May 1617 provided that (apart from the proportion of copper, mentioned above) the rent to the Society for the first two years should be 'one pepper Corne at the Feast of Easter if it be demaunded'; for the third year it was to be £40, paid at Lady Day at 'the now dwelling howse of Sir Richard Smythe knight, scituat in Colman streete in London, or at the howse of any other the Treasurer for the tyme being' of the Society; then for the next seven years the rent was to be £20, to be paid at Lady Day and Michaelmas 'by even and equal porcōns'; finally, for the remaining eleven years, the rent was to rise to £30. As it turned out, of course, there was no copper, and the explanation of the discrepancy between these figures and Pettus's £400 may be that when it was realized that the metal in the mines was silver-bearing lead (but surely this must have been known all along?), a higher rent was stipulated, or a fixed proportion of the silver in lieu of rent.[3] There is no documentary evidence confirming such a surmise, but possibly a royalty on the silver, being customary, was taken for granted. Some support for this may be seen in a memorandum among the Earl of Middlesex's papers, endorsed 'Silver Mines 1622', which, after remarking that 'the kinge of Spaine in the riche mines of the weste Indies hathe but a fivethe

[1] J. Pettus, op. cit. p. 53.

[2] The Mines Royal Society was revived after the Restoration, and was amalgamated with its sister company, the Mineral and Battery Works. Efforts were made to resume active silver mining, and at the request of Prince Rupert (then Governor of the company) and Ashley Cooper Sir John Pettus wrote *Fodinae Regales* to publicize its operations. Cf. *D.N.B.* s.v. 'Pettus', and W. R. Scott, op. cit. ii. 403.

[3] The company had to pay the Crown a tenth part of the silver from its mines (W. R. Scott, op. cit. ii. 384).

parte of all undertakers in thos mines royall where his officers disburse not all charges', goes on to suggest that as 'the mines of England royall are nothings so riche . . . the undertakers shall iustly paye the sixthe parte of all silver [which] shall be made out of all mines royall into his Majesties exchequer halfe yearly and undergoe all charges themselves'. The Lord Treasurer, Middlesex, who did so much to improve the King's income, was evidently alive to the advantages of exploiting the royal mines, and apparently thought of going into partnership himself, for the memorandum suggests that 'a graunt for xx^{tie} yeares more or lesse' should be made to 'the Lord Treasurer, Sir Hugh Middleton and Sir Edward Grevill payinge the sixte parte as before', with a further rather obscurely worded proviso, by way of safeguarding or increasing the King's revenue, which appears to mean that unless the King's future annual income from the sixth part exceeded by fifty per cent. his average annual receipts ('so muche . . . as hath bin payed communibus annis') from Sir Hugh in the past, the patentees were to make up their payments to that amount.[1]

Pettus's figure of £400 a year might conceivably represent the averaging up of royalties on the silver, but there is no evidence that the scheme in the memorandum was adopted. Nor in fact is it likely to have been, for shortly afterwards Middlesex was overthrown by the efforts of the Duke of Buckingham and his courtier friends, and it is significant that the lease obtained by Myddelton from the Crown in 1625, which, besides granting the mines free of money rent, expressly refers to the King waiving the customary royalty of one tenth of the silver produced, was stated to have been obtained by Buckingham's 'mediation'. It seems that Myddelton knew whom to cultivate when he wanted favours from the King. At the same time, Pettus's figure is not inconsistent with what we are told by Thomas Bushell, Sir Hugh's successor at the mines. Bushell had first to buy out Lady Myddelton's interest by paying her a year's rent down, and he then took on the remainder of Sir Hugh's lease at the same rent. This was in 1636, and for four years, he tells us, he laboured to drain the mines of the water in which they had lain 'drowned' since

[1] Sackville MS. (H.M.C.), no. 8174.

Myddelton's death. Then, when success came and he was making good profits, he petitioned the King for a new lease, offering an increase of rent to £1,000 a year.[1] But Bushell was incurably optimistic about the prospects of his mining schemes, and his statements were often so highly coloured by his imagination that it would be unsafe to rely on his figures without corroboration. In any case it looks as if he defaulted on his rent to Lady Myddelton, for in July 1641 she was bringing an action against him.[2]

As in the surveying and construction of the New River, Myddelton engaged technical experts to manage or supervise operations at the mines and smelting works. We catch a glimpse of one of these in a letter to Sir John Wynn of Gwydir from his son Owen in London, dated 12 February 1621/2.[3] Sir John had evidently raised some lead on his own land, for Owen writes that 'the chapman Basbie' would take three pounds of it on trial. 'He is well reported of and should have had all Hugh Myddelton's works in Cardiganshire at a certain rent, but one Baynard stepped in before him and took the work and afterwards left it, and now Hugh Myddelton would "piece" again with this Basbie for that work, but he would not take it.' Who Baynard was we do not know; he may conceivably have been the German miner Barnard who had been prospecting in Cornwall in the previous century.[4] Walter Basbie, *alias* Basbee or Barksby, was an experienced metallurgist who had been employed in Bevis Bulmer's mines in Yorkshire in the later years of Elizabeth's reign, and under James I became 'assay-master' to the Goldsmiths' Company, through which presumably Myddelton made his acquaintance. Later the King sent him on a visit 'to the emperor of Russia to make him a standard of gold and silver in his mint in the City of Muscovia, and no sooner was this done than he was commanded by the Emperor to refine the gold of a rich copper mine in Siberia, five hundred miles beyond the Volga', a journey which led to his

---

[1] T. Bushell, *A Just and True Remonstrance of H.M. Mines Royal in . . . Wales* (1641), p. 7.

[2] *House of Lords MSS.* xi (New Series), Addenda 1514–1714, p. 261.

[3] *Cal. Wynn Papers*, no. 1008.

[4] On Barnard cf. A. L. Rowse, *Tudor Cornwall* (1941), p. 56; M. B. Donald, *Elizabethan Copper* (1955), pp. 303, 306, 314.

being taken prisoner by the Tartars. He was subsequently ex-
changed and returned to England, and in his old age we hear of
him again at the mines in Cardiganshire and on Mendip, when
his advice was sought by Thomas Bushell.[1]

Myddelton apparently worked five mines in north Cardiganshire—Cwmsymlog, Cwmerfin, Goginan, Cwmystwyth, and Allt-
y-Crib near Talybont, of which Cwmsymlog was probably the
most important. These and other Welsh names proved altogether
too much for seventeenth-century Englishmen. Cwmsymlog,
for example was variously spelt Coomsumlock, Coomsumblock,
Cumsumlock, Consumlock, and Consomlogh. Best of all, and
very appropriate for a mining venture, was 'Come-some-luck'!
Myddelton was not deterred by the popular belief that ore from
deeper levels was of poor quality, and he sank shafts to reach the
ore that his predecessors had failed to touch. To overcome the
usual difficulties from flooding he installed some kind of pumping
engine at Cwmsymlog, which according to Waller worked
'several yards under water'.[2] Even so, it seems, he worked 'but
one top level of a few yards . . . called to this day Sr Hugh's
Level'; but even if his workings were shallow compared with the
mines opened later, he evidently got considerably deeper than
anyone before him. According to Lewis Morris, Myddelton had
two water-engines, 'one in each brook that cross the work,
whereby he wrought it (as may be guessed by the hillocks) to
about 70 or 80 yards in depth. Some remains of these engines',
he adds, 'were found in cutting through the work to bring a
Level to the east . . . as some old miners still alive can testify.'[3]

We need not suppose that Myddelton himself invented, or had
a hand in inventing, these engines. They may be the engines
referred to in a message from the King to Solicitor-General Heath,
dated 2 July 1624, authorizing him to complete, with the assistance of Secretary Conway and Sir Richard Weston, the contracts initiated between Myddelton and his partner Sir Bevis

[1] See his affidavit in *Rep. H.M.C.* vii, App. 81*b*, and my biography of Bushell, *The
Superlative Prodigall* (Bristol, 1932).

[2] (W. Waller), *Report on the Lead and Silver Mines of Bwlch yr Eskir-hir &c.* (?1709),
p. 6.

[3] N.L.W. Add. MS. 603E, p. 3.

Thelwall, and a certain Thomas Russell, 'for working the mines royal in Cardiganshire with the assistance of some invention of Russell's'.[1] Other inventors were also engaged on similar lines, for when in 1623 Myddelton had applied for a patent for 'a newly invented waterwork' he was informed that a patent for the same or a similar machine had just been granted to a Lieutenant Garlick.[2] When Thomas Bushell took over the mines after Sir Hugh's death, he maintained that Sir Hugh, who had worked downwards from the heights of the hills, had never reached far below 'the Superficies of the Earth, the workes being drowned with water before they could sinke to the best of the veyne'.[3] Bushell, on the other hand, declared that he could overcome these difficulties by driving adits from the lowest possible levels in the valleys, and that this was a revolutionary advance in mining technique. In fact, however, there was nothing new in the use of adits (we hear of them in the Middle Ages);[4] as we shall see, Myddelton's men themselves proposed to drive an adit to drain one of the workings, and presumably did so, as it is marked on Pettus's diagram of Cwmsymlog, though with the note that it 'carried but that level'. We do not know how effective it was, and Bushell may well have been justified in his claim to have succeeded in reaching greater depths than Sir Hugh; but according to Waller 'the Patentees endeavoured to bring up an Addit, to go under this Work, . . . but they struck much short of reaching his (i.e. Myddelton's) Bottoms: And though that Vein hath been attempted by many, yet it never was recover'd till now, since Sir Hugh Middleton's death'.[5] The truth is hard to ascertain, because each of these writers sought for propaganda purposes to magnify his own achievements.

According to Pettus 'there was some Dispute between Sir Hugh Middleton and Sir Richard Price concerning the Mines

---

[1] *Cal. S.P.D. 1623–5*, pp. 289, 290.

[2] *Cal. S.P.D. 1619–23*, p. 570; Secretary Conway to Sir Hugh, 25 Apr. 1623. Only three days previously Conway had instructed the Attorney-General to prepare a patent for Lieut. Lawrence Garlick 'for the sole benefit of his new invention of a mill for draining drowned lands, coal-pits, etc. for milling cloth, grinding corn, and other uses'—evidently a most versatile machine! (Ibid., p. 566).

[3] T. Bushell, op. cit., p. 22.   [4] Cf. L. F. Salzman, op. cit., p. 53.

[5] (W. Waller), *Report on the Lead and Silver Mines, &c.*, p. 6.

at Tallabont . . ., whether Royal or not Royal', the date he gives being 'about the year 1639'. The judgement in the famous Case of Mines[1] in Elizabeth's reign established the principle that a mine was royal if the value of the gold or silver exceeded the cost of refining and the value of the base metal from which it was extracted, but if the quantity of gold or silver were less than this, the mine was not royal but belonged to the owner of the ground. Now the ore from Talybont, as we have seen, was said to be poor in silver, and there seems nothing inherently improbable in the local landlord claiming that this mine was not royal, and so was not covered by Myddelton's lease. But Pettus's account cannot be accurate as it stands, for by 1639 Myddelton had been dead for eight years. While working the mines Myddelton lived from time to time at the house called Lodge, subsequently known as Lodge Park, which stood on an isolated wooded hill near the Dovey estuary, about three miles from Talybont. It belonged to Sir John Pryse (or Price) of Gogerddan, but so far from quarrelling the families were on such friendly terms that Pryse's son Richard, who later became a baronet, married Myddelton's daughter Hester. The dispute Pettus referred to was in all probability one which broke out in 1641–2 between Sir Richard Pryse and Myddelton's successor Bushell.[2]

Myddelton's work, nevertheless, cannot have been without anxieties and opposition. We do not know what were the 'discouraging rumours' to which James I alluded in a letter written to Sir Hugh from Theobalds on 31 March 1623, when the King urged him to 'continue his endeavours for advancing the work of the Royal Mines, which shall be rewarded in due time';[3] but they may well refer to the claims of rivals who, when news of Myddelton's success became known, were anxious to displace him. The King promised that he would 'never place the work in other hands without recompensing him', and the government

---

[1] In the Court of Exchequer, Hilary 10 Eliz. (1 Plowden, 310–40), when a copper mine on the Earl of Northumberland's property at Newlands in the Lake District was claimed as royal.

[2] See *Rep. H.M.C.* v, App. 16a, 21b; *L.J.* iv. 700b, v. 53a; also my *The Superlative Prodigall*, p. 53.

[3] *Cal. S.P.D. 1619–23*, p. 544.

support he enjoyed as a result of his connexion with the Court may well have been needed. Thus later in the same year the King sent instructions to the President and Council of Wales, authorizing them to 'apprehend all persons found encroaching' on Sir Hugh's mines,[1] and in the following month he was summoned to attend a Privy Council meeting at which certain rules and a proclamation for the mines were under consideration.[2] Opposition had been encountered, for as early as 8 April 1618 the Council had armed him with an 'open warrant' which, in consideration of the risk that the mines 'being planted in a remoate place and countrey may haply finde some opposicion by persons ill affected that preferr their owne private ends and profitt before the common good', called on the local authorities to assist him, 'his deputie and servauntes upon all occasions as they shall have cause to repare unto you in that behalf'. The authorities were also to assist him if required in 'governing so many sortes of workemen as are to be imployed therein, amongst whom it cannot bee but some will prove mutinous and disordered, or forsake the worke without lycence or just cause, and that oftentimes when they have receaved their wages before haunde'.[3] There were no trade unions in those days!

We need not be surprised that Myddelton, and Bushell after him, coming in from outside with government backing, met local opposition and hostility. Until the law was changed in 1689 by the Mines Royal Act,[4] the Crown or its lessees could open and work mines producing gold or silver wherever they chose, while the owners of the soil complained that they got 'no advantage nor the least share of the profit; but on the contrary, their lands were torn up to the very Bowels, and covered with Heaps of Rubbish, and High-ways were made over their Corn and Pasture Land, without paying any Consideration for the same.[5] Besides local opposition, Myddelton was also put to considerable trouble by

---

[1] *Cal. S.P.D. 1623–5*, p. 75 (8 Sept. 1623).

[2] Ibid., p. 88; cf. p. 99. This was probably not the proclamation referred to above (p. 110) but a warning to 'encroachers'.

[3] *Acts P.C. Jan. 1618–June 1619*, p. 100.   [4] See below, p. 129, n. 1.

[5] (W. Waller), *A Familiar Discourse or Dialogue . . . concerning the Mine-Adventure*, p. 96.

the pretensions of a Dutchman called Levin (or Lewin) van Hack (or Hake), who approached the Privy Council in the spring of 1623 with a claim that he could produce twice as much lead from the ore as Myddelton could, that he could refine the silver it contained more quickly, and that he could do so by using 'sea or pit coal' instead of charcoal. This was shortly after Dud Dudley had found a way of smelting iron with pit coal, and various attempts were made about this time to use coal for smelting other metals. Myddelton himself, as appeared when the trials with van Hack took place, was using coal, but he had to mix it with wood-fuel. Bushell later experimented with peat as well as with what he called 'sea-coale charked', and claimed to have been successful, but it remains doubtful whether any of the attempts to find substitutes for wood and charcoal were really effective until nearly the end of the seventeenth century, when a new type of furnace came into use.[1]

The Government, always in financial straits, jumped at any chance, however improbable, of raising more cash, and the Lord Treasurer, Middlesex, promised on behalf of the King that if his claims were substantiated van Hack should be 'made a denizen, have the profit of his invention for thirteen years, and become master workman of the mines royal'.[2] Arrangements should be made 'that the Dutchman and Sir Hugh shall each have two tons . . . of ore from the mines . . . and shall each have a fair trial, under oversight of three knights of the country, that the true riches of the mine and skilfulness of the working may be known, without disturbing the present works'.[3] The umpires actually selected to supervise the trials were two experts, the Cornishman Sir Francis Godolphin and Sir Thomas Stafford, 'whose experience and skill we know to be good in theise minnerall matters', and two local knights, 'Sir Henry Williams and Sir John Lewys, being neare dwellers to the place', or any two of these four.

---

[1] For van Hack's claim see *Cal. S.P.D. 1619–23*, p. 593. A company for 'smelting down lead with pit-coal and sea-coal' was incorporated in 1692 (*Selden Soc.*, vol. 28, pp. 228–30). For smelting experiments in the sixteenth and seventeenth centuries with various fuels see the references in G. R. Lewis, *The Stannaries* (Harvard, 1907), p. 24, note 4.

[2] *Cal. S.P.D. 1619–23*, p. 594.

[3] *Cal. S.P.D. Addenda 1580–1625*, p. 653 (18 Apr. 1623).

There was a well-known Sir Francis Godolphin who did much to develop the Cornish tin industry, and who also played a notable part in the defence of the Isles of Scilly and west Cornwall against Spanish raiders, but this cannot have been he, for he died in 1608. I think it must have been his youngest son, who inherited his father's tin interests on the death of his eldest brother Sir William in 1613. He became Recorder of Helston in 1620 and died in 1640. There was also another Francis Godolphin, to whom Hobbes dedicated *Leviathan*. He was a grandson of the first Sir Francis, nephew of the second, and brother of the poet Sidney Godolphin, but he can be ruled out, for he was only eighteen in 1623. The identity of Sir Thomas Stafford is doubtful. Possibly he was the Stafford who served under George Carew in the Irish wars, and was the reputed author of *Pacata Hibernia*. He might have had some acquaintance with metallurgy from his appointment as assistant to Carew when in 1608 the latter became Master of the Ordnance.[1]

These umpires were instructed to 'repaire to the said mynes', and in their presence van Hack was to be supplied with 'two or three tonnes of ore, either out of the storehouse of Sir Hugh Middleton, or out of the myne itself, which in your judgments shall seem fittest for the certainer tryall, and you are then to view and see what quantity of lead is melted out of the same proporcion of ore and what quantity of silver is refyned out of the same lead, and likewise to examine what quantity of lead Sir Hugh Middleton's servants hath [*sic*] ever melted out of the same proporcion . . .' After the trial the umpires were 'speedily to certifie what he hath made good according to his articles and wherein he is defective together with your opinions of him touching his skill and experiments and also what other services in those works you shall understand in your judgment to be of use for his Majestie'.[2]

The trial duly took place in the presence of Sir Francis

[1] On the Godolphins see Richard Carew, *Survey of Cornwall* (1602), f. 153; J. L. Vivian, *Visitations of Cornwall* (1887), p. 184; F. G. Marsh, *The Godolphins* (1930), p. 7; see also A. L. Rowse, *Tudor Cornwall* (1941), pp. 54–55, 399–406. On Sir Thomas Stafford see *D.N.B.* s.v.

[2] *Acts P.C. July 1621–May 1623*, p. 514 (31 May 1623).

Godolphin and Sir John Lewis, who sent to the Lord Treasurer a detailed report of the proceedings, dated 30 July 1623.[1] On arrival at the works they caused samples of 'the ore then lying in several heapes neare the melting howses to bee brought out of everie heape, according to the quantitie of each heape of ore a proportionable part', had them 'well mingled together, and thereof delivered out by weight one Tonne and a halfe unto the melters of Sr Hugh Middleton, and one other Tonne and halfe of the said mingled oare unto Levin van Hake'. Similar quantities of 'the new oare of the latest breaking at the mine' were also mixed together and delivered to the competitors, so that each had three tons to work with. Van Hake was not yet ready, so Myddelton's men were set to work. On Monday, 14 July, between 8 o'clock in the morning and 7 o'clock in the evening, using 'twoe severall fornaces or hearthes', they finished melting down the first ton and a half of ore, producing from it 'tenn barrs or Sowes of rich Lead weighing in the whole Tenn hundreds, 3 quarters and seaventeene pounds weight'. On Wednesday, 16 July, they went to work on their second ton and a half of ore. It took them from 7 o'clock in the morning until 9.30 at night, 'in which tyme they produced in both fornaces or hearthes eleaven Barrs or Sowes of rich lead; which weighed eleaven hundred one quarter and fourteene pound'. The total yield in the two days' smelting of the three tons of ore was thus 1 ton 2 cwt. 1 qr. 3 lb. of rich lead. The fuel consumed consisted of 31[2] hogsheads of 'white cole' and 'of Pitt or Stone cole neere about 5 barrells', costing altogether 'as neere as wee can estimate' sixteen shillings; for 'they have agreed with the Colliers after the rate of tenn shillings for the white cole that they shall use to the making or melting downe of each tonne of Lead, and their stone or pitt cole stands them about tenn shillings the Tonne weight'.

The next step was to assay a small sample of the rich lead, which as a result was estimated to contain 77 oz. of fine silver per ton, indicating an expected yield of $85\frac{1}{2}$ oz. 3 dwt. 6 gr. of fine

---

[1] Sackville MS. (H.M.C.), no. 8897. In *Rep. H.M.C.* vii, App. p. 254, it is wrongly dated 1625.

[2] The manuscript is torn at this point, but I think this is the correct figure.

silver from the whole amount of the lead. On Thursday, 17 July, the lead was 'brought to the Refyning Howse and there refined in our presence which yeilded a Cake or Slabb of silver that weighed 84 oz. and there was gayned besides out of the Chincks and Clefts in the Teast one ounce and half more'. The total yield therefore was '85½ oz. of Teast silver worth about 5s. and 3d. the ownce'— a result remarkably close to the assay. At the same time 17 cwt. 3 qr. 26 lb. of poor lead was 'reduced . . . out of the Litharge of the aforesaid lead', apart from 'lead remayning in the Teast and sweepings, which could not then be reduced by the same fornace.' An assay of the poor lead showed that it still contained 5½ oz. 6 dwt. of silver per ton 'after it is refined and reduced back again out of Litharge into poore lead'. The judges explained that they could not estimate the labour cost 'for the getting, dressing, carrying and melting of this oare, . . . for that their workmen are hired by the yeare', but they estimated that 'the charge of fewell which they use for the refyning and reducing of a Tonne of Lead, doth not stand them in much above a marke'.

Levin van Hack was then called upon again, but he still was not ready. He 'pretended that hee would be readie within a daie or twoe at the furthest, which time being come he yett held us on in expectacōn the space of a weeke more with pretending something to be expected before he could goe on with his Tryall'. Meanwhile, however, 'his fornace being hott, to satisfie himself hee went about to make a tryall therein of some small quantitie of oare, which hee findinge toe worke noe effect, pretended the insufficiencie of his pann or hearth in his reverberating fornace and soe putt out his fire'. Then he tried again with 'another pann made of claye', but 'when he had continued for the space of Forty howers or more and that his fornace beganne to bee of a good heate, his pann which had remayned whole and entire all this tyme, as hee pretended, unfortunately broke'. The umpires felt sure, however, 'noe other bodie being then in the roome, but the doore found shutt on him', that he broke it himself 'of sett purpose . . . , as uppon view of the pann afterwards by apparent tokens wee might easilie gather, which confirmed us in our iealousies formerlie on iust grounds conceived of his

insufficiencie to performe what hee had undertaken'. He never made
any pretence of refining silver from lead, 'being as ignorant therein as in the rest'; he was in fact 'altogether unfitt to bee any waies
employed in matters of this nature', and was 'a meere Impostor
and great Abuser'.

So much for Levin van Hack. Godolphin and Lewis concluded
their report with some remarks about the mine itself. They
found 'a verie hopeful load [lode] . . . of a good length running
almost east and west and yeilding good plentie of oare; neere
the grasse or daie[1] and very hopefull in the sinking to continue
good. In some places wee find it at the depth of 4 or 5 fathomes
to bee almost twoe foote broad verie well powdred in the oare;
in other places a foote broad, and other some but halfe a foot and
yeilding verie poore oare; in some other places againe, not soe
broad.' The mine was 'likelie to prove a worke of verie good
continuance if it bee well managed and directed'. In the past there
had been defects in this respect, 'in regard the workers have not
been soe provident as they should have bene in the manner of
getting their oare, whereby the worke in a short space will
become altogether unable to be wrought unles it bee tymelie
prevented, and an Auditt [adit] bee speedilie brought in to the
vayne for the unwatering thereof, which wee find they are now
about to doe'. The number of workmen employed was '150 . . .
or upwards, who have and doe weekelie land upwards of 20
tonnes of oare'. Future progress might vary 'according as they
shall meete with hardnes or softnes in their working and according as the same goes broader or narrower in their driving or
sincking', but there was 'good probabilitie and likelihood of
other vaines and lodes not farr distant from these as indeed the
Countrey discovers itselfe in sundrie places to be verie fertile in
lead vaines, although divers of them prove but poore in silver'.
Some, however, 'might be wrought to turne to good advantage
to the Labourers and Adventurers, And might be an occasion of
farther discoveries which might redound to the benefitt of his
Ma[tie] and the state'.

Levin van Hack was not the only adventurer attracted by

---

[1] i.e. near the surface.

reports or rumours of the money to be made in Wales. On 29 March 1624 William Gomeldon addressed a petition to the King, in which the opening recital declared that his Majesty was 'pleased to allow Lavine van Hackt 100 tun of oare at 4^{libs} a tun,[1] in regarde of his pretence to melte and refine a greater quantitie thereof than Sir Hugh Midleton by his course of working is able to performe'. The petitioner, being 'informed there is Ore in quantitie sufficient for us all', asked leave to purchase ore at the same rate, 'and I shall undertake . . . to melte and refine a greater quantitie in less space . . . than they do, And yett without the preiudice or hindrance of either of them in the least, vizt. 65 tun of Ore weekly, for which I will give yor Matie 250^{libs} a weeke, which doth arise to 1000^{libs} a month'.[2]

It is unlikely that anything more came of either Gomeldon's or van Hack's claims. At any rate there is no further record of their activities, whereas we have seen that in 1625 Myddelton secured from the King the confirmation, renewal, and prolongation of his lease. We read that he 'hath allready brought the said Mynes and minerall workes . . . to that good perfeccōn that if by our gracious assistance he maye be therein incouraged the same may hereafter prove very proffitable to the Commonwealth in generall and very benificiall to our heires and successors in particular'. Myddelton had asked the King not only to 'confirme and graunt unto him the said Mynes and our interest in and to the same' but also 'under our Great Seale of England to authorise some persons of ranck and quallitie to take the care and government of the said Mynes and of all workemen and others to be imployed'. The grant was to Myddelton personally (and his executors, administrators, and assigns), but according to Scott he formed a separate company, 'known as the Mines Royal of Wales', and distinct from the original Society of the Mines Royal, to work the Welsh mines. This is an inference from a clause in his will, directing that his 'partes and shares in the Mines Royall in the principallitie of

---

[1] I do not know what this means. One would have thought that the report from Godolphin and Lewis nine months previously would have finished van Hack's pretensions entirely, but on the plea that his refining technique had never actually been tested he may possibly have asked and got leave to purchase ore at a preferential rate.

[2] Sackville MS. (H.M.C.), no. 8990.

Wales' should be sold to pay his debts and legacies, but we need not interpret it as implying an incorporated company, as distinct from a partnership.[1]

The new lease from the Crown empowered him to open mines 'as well within our own mannors . . . lands grounds and possessions as also within the grounds lands and possessions of any of our subiects'. Mines were not to be dug 'under any Castles forts fortresses . . .' nor 'within any dwelling houses or edifices belonging to any of our subiects without the good will and consent of such as have power to licence them so to doe', and then only provided proper compensation were paid. 'If the veyne shalbe found to runn and extend itself without the limits and bounds aforesaid', Myddelton might 'follow and worke after the same veyne into all other places (excepting Mynes opened by others in the same ground . . . before discovery) paying to the owners, farmers, etc. double the value of the damage'. He was further to have power 'to take up at reasonable wages[2] and prices anywhere within this realme of England and dominion of Wales all manner of Artificers and Workemen (not at that time imployed in any other our mynes royall) and all manner of timber wood underwood coales turves peats . . . instruments stuffe and necessaries whatsoever'; and sheriffs, justices of the peace, bailiffs, constables 'and all other our officers and ministers' were called on to aid and assist him in his work. All the silver produced was to be brought once a month to the Mint in the Tower of London, where it would be paid for at 'such price in ready monye as silver of the lyke fynenesse and goodnes is worth and as shalbe then usually given for the same'. Finally, Myddelton's title was to be good in any court of law, although the sites of particular mines were not exactly specified in the lease, and 'notwithstanding the

---

1 W. R. Scott, *The Constitution and Finance of . . . Joint-Stock Companies* (Cambridge, 1911), ii. 401; *Wills from Doctors' Commons* (Camden Soc., 1863, for 1862), p. 95.

2 We have no information about the wages earned by Myddelton's workmen at the mines, as distinct from those employed on the New River, but according to J. E. Thorold Rogers (*Six Centuries of Work and Wages* (1884), pp. 391, 427) in the early seventeenth century an artisan (a skilled man) earned about a shilling a day, a labourer about 9*d*. Pettus tells us that in his time 'the myners are to finde themselves Iron, Steel and Candles at their own charge. The Masters are only to finde Tymber for the works, and Ropes, Pumps, Tubs and Sieves to cleanse the Oar and Bags to carry it to the Mills' (op. cit., p. 40).

not reserving of the tenth parte of the silver of those Mynes to the use of us our Heires and successors according to the proclamacōn before mencōned or according to any agreement made with us or the . . . late Queene Elizabeth by the Governors Assistants and Societye of and for the Mynes Royall'.

Myddelton's request that the mines should be put under the control of 'some persons of ranck and quallitie' was answered early in Charles I's reign by a Commission from the new King[1] to a large panel of authorities, ranging from eminent persons such as the Archbishop of Canterbury, the Lord Treasurer, the Lord President of the Council, the Lord Chamberlain, and others, down to a list of over forty local personages, including the justices for the Welsh and Border counties, Sir Hugh himself, Sir Bevis Thelwall, Sir Francis Godolphin, and the German engineer Daniel Höchstetter. After reciting the confirmation of the lease, the 'Discouragements happening by the interposition of others, whoe have attempted to buylde uppon his Foundation', and the lack of an adequate supply of labour properly under control, the commissioners were authorized 'to make, ordeyne and establish all such Orders, Ordynances, Lawes and Rules, for the well orderinge and governings of the Workemen and Labourers', as they or any three of them should think fit. They could summon workmen and labourers before them, hear complaints, and punish 'such as shall stubbornlie and refractorilie oppose themselves against Us and our Royal Pleasure in this behalfe'. Any who obstructed Sir Hugh or his agents or servants while digging, cutting or carrying away 'Stones, Clay, Turffs, Peates, Heath or other Materyalls . . . upon anie Wastes, Commons or Mountaynes . . .' were to be liable to imprisonment; and if the Commissioners thought the offence 'to deserve a more exemplary Punishment', offenders were to be brought before the Privy Council, or before the Council of the Marches of Wales.

Besides penal clauses, the Commission sought to improve working conditions. Miners were to be exempt from proceedings for debts below the value of forty shillings, and local inhabitants were to be encouraged to bring in 'all manner of Corne, Graine,

[1] Dated 12 May 1625; printed in Rymer, *Foedera*, xviii. 66–72.

Victualls, Provisions and other Necessaries', with penalties for conspiring to raise prices. On the other hand, miners were to be prevented from buying 'all manner of strong Ale and strong Beer whatsoever within the Compass of five, fower or three Myles of the Place or Places in which the said Mines are or shalbe wrought'. Other clauses confirmed Myddelton's powers to impress labour, and also to take up 'by waie of Impresse, att reasonable and usuall Prices', materials such as 'Timber, Wood, Coales and all other manner of Fewell', as well as 'Horses, Oxen, Cartes and Carriages', and he was to have 'free Libertie of Ingresse, Egresse and Regresse . . . into through and from all manner of Grounds through which it shalbe convenyent . . . to have Passage'.

We learn further that 'divers Abuses have been committed . . . in erecting of Weares uppon the famous River of *Dovye*, where the Sea ebbeth and floweth, to the great Hindrance of Our Workes in the Mynes aforesaide, And also that the High Waies and Bridgs, between *Machmullett* and the *Garreck* . . .[1] are much impayred and broken'. Accordingly 'our Commissioners for Sewers of and for those parts' were to have the weirs demolished, and the J.P.s for the counties of Cardigan, Merioneth, and Montgomery were to have the highways repaired. It also appears that 'divers Woods and Underwoods . . . for the Use of the said Mynes and Mynerall Works', which Sir Hugh had bought and paid for, were being 'deteyned' from him. The Commissioners, or any three of them, were to deal by summons and inquiry with this and other misdeeds such as 'defacing and pulling down of any Milles, Melting Houses, Fyning Houses or other Buyldings'; they were also to find out 'what Waterwheeles, Bellowes, Tooles, Instruments or other Materialls . . . have bynn ymbeaseled and made away, and by whome, and to what value'. Delinquents were to make restitution, and if they refused were to be referred to the Privy Council or the Council of the Marches of Wales.

According to Pettus, Myddelton made such a success of his mines that 'he cleared monthly the summe of £2,000'.[2] In the

---

[1] Machynlleth and Garreg.   [2] J. Pettus, *Fodinae Regales*, p. 33.

absence of detailed accounts, however, and in view of Pettus's other inaccuracies, we should receive this figure with caution.[1] The same applies to the other large round figures often repeated in this connexion—the £50,000 worth of silver which Myddelton was said (by Bushell) to have sent to the Mint during his tenure of the mines, and the 100 oz. of silver per ton of lead that he got from Cwmsymlog. This last figure is almost certainly an exaggeration. Some selected pieces of ore may conceivably have been as rich as this,[2] but we have seen that the lead refined at the trial with van Hack gave 77 oz. of silver per ton, and in later years even less than this was expected, though Cwmsymlog had the reputation of being the richest mine in the district. In the early eighteenth century it was said to produce over 60 oz. of silver per ton, and this was then regarded as 'a rich vein indeed'; other mines, which were described as 'very rich in silver', yielded 'above forty, and some above fifty ounces of silver in each Tun of lead'.[3]

Though precise figures elude us, we need not doubt that Myddelton made a good deal of money. As in his other undertakings, his success was due not to any special technical skill or training, but to his energy and perseverance, and his determination not to be defeated by any obstacles, whether natural or human. At the same time he was no 'hard-faced' business man. He could conscript labourers, it is true, but the seventeenth century saw nothing wrong in this. It was typical of his devoutness and his care for others' welfare that he built a chapel for his workmen at Cwmsymlog. It is marked on Pettus's plan of the workings, but by his time it was 'decayed'.[4]

When the mines were in regular production the silver from them was so plentiful that the coins made from it bore the Welsh

---

[1] A rough calculation on the basis of the figures given in the report of the van Hack trial points to gross takings of about £1,500 a month from the silver, so that Pettus's figure, including all the mines and the sale of lead, may not be excessive. But 'cleared' presumably indicates net profit after paying wages, costs of fuel and materials, transport, &c., and these cannot be estimated with any accuracy.

[2] Cf. R. Hunt, 'Notices of the History of the Lead Mines of Cardiganshire', in *Memoirs of the Geological Survey of G.B.* II. ii (1848), p. 641.

[3] W. Shiers, *A Familiar Discourse or Dialogue concerning the Mine Adventure* (1705), pp. 3, 32. The real author was said to be Sir Humphrey Mackworth (*C.J.* xvi. 365).

[4] J. Pettus, op. cit., p. 35.

feathers as a distinguishing mark.[1] This may have originated in James's personal interest in Myddelton; the mark was continued under Charles I, and when Bushell, in order to avoid the expense of conveying the bullion to London, obtained leave to establish a mint at Aberystwyth, all the coins minted there were similarly marked with the feathers.

After Sir Hugh's death in 1631 the mines soon fell into neglect and became flooded again, until five years later Bushell took over from his widow the remainder of his lease. It seems that Bushell was introduced to the Welsh mines by Sir Francis Godolphin, who had visited them at the time of the van Hack affair and had seen their value. Bushell had recently exhibited his flair for constructing 'waterworks' at the once-famous Rock at Enstone, in Oxfordshire, and may well have seemed to Godolphin a suitable man to undertake the draining of the mines. Bushell and Godolphin accordingly started as partners, but soon afterwards Godolphin died, and Bushell then entered into partnership with an Oxfordshire neighbour, Edmund Goodyear of Heythrop. At first he met with the usual setbacks, but he subsequently claimed to have been even more successful than Myddelton had been, and the establishment of the mint at Aberystwyth is in itself a testimonial to the dimensions of his enterprise. Bushell's activities at the mines were cut short by the Civil War, in which he participated as an ardent royalist, and when the mines had been captured by the parliamentary forces he lost possession of them. After that we hear little of them for a time, but it appears that later the management of them was once more in the hands of the Mines Royal Society. Work was in progress when John Ray visited them in 1658 and 1662, and Sir John Pettus, who was Deputy-Governor of the Society, gives a lengthy account of the apparatus there in 1667. There was another burst of activity in the last decade of the century, when very rich ore was discovered at Esgair-hir, on the estate of Sir Carbery Pryse of Gogerddan. He fought the claims of the Society of the Mines Royal, and with the

[1] Llewelyn Jones, 'The Welsh Mint', in *Economica*, vi (1926), pp. 310–21. The coins minted were the angel (worth 10s.), the crown, half-crown, shilling, sixpence, threepence, twopence, and penny. The king gave orders to the Master of the Mint that all the Welsh silver should be coined separately from 3 Sept. 1623.

aid of other influential landlords procured the enactment of the Mines Royal Act,[1] which ended the Society's monopoly. Fresh discoveries were then made, and a number of new mines were rapidly opened. Sir Carbery died shortly afterwards, but Sir Humphrey Mackworth of Neath, who acquired Sir Carbery's interests, floated a company called the Mine Adventurers, the prospects for which were glowingly advertised by his manager, William Waller, a Yorkshireman who had previously been employed by Sir Carbery Pryse. Waller had visions of establishing a 'Welsh Potosi' among the foothills of Plynlimmon,[2] but disputes and lawsuits followed, and the scheme, in which shares had been distributed as lottery-prizes, collapsed with heavy losses to people who had subscribed to it.[3]

Later there was some revival of mining, and argentiferous galena was worked at numerous places until well into the second half of the nineteenth century. A kind of shareholders' guide, published by a Liverpool firm of brokers, describes no less than 104 mines that were in operation in Cardiganshire about 1870,[4] but after about 1875 there was a considerable fall in the price of lead, due largely to the competition of lead imported from abroad, and by the end of the century many of these mines had closed down. Cwmsymlog, the chief scene of Myddelton's work, was finally abandoned in 1901, and by 1914 the mining industry in the county was practically dead. There was a brief and feeble revival in the Rheiddol and Ystwyth valleys during the First World War, but by 1922 the last two lead mines in the district had been closed.[5]

[1] 1 William and Mary, c. 30. The effect was to empower freeholders to work the mines of base metal on their own land, without licence from the Society, irrespective of the amount of gold or silver produced.

[2] Cf. his pamphlet, *An Essay on the Value of the Mines, late of Sir Carbery Price* (1698). This was not a new idea. Bushell, with characteristic optimism, talked of making 'a second Indies' in Wales, and the poet Randolph mentioned
'Plots to bring Spain to England and confine
King Philip's Indies unto Middleton's Mine'
(T. Randolph, *Poems* (5th edn., 1664), p. 105).

[3] See W. R. Scott, op. cit. ii. 443–58. The charter of the company is printed in *Selden Soc.*, vol. 28, pp. 243–8.

[4] *The Mines of Cardiganshire, Montgomeryshire and Shropshire* (quoted above, p. 103, n. 4, and p. 106, n. 2). It is undated, but is listed in the B.M. catalogue as '? 1870'.

[5] Cf. the articles by K. Carpenter and W. J. Lewis referred to in notes 3 and 4, p. 101, above.

VIII

THE LAST OF THE MYDDELTONS

It has sometimes been said that Sir Hugh Myddelton died, if not a poor man, at any rate in reduced circumstances, but I think this conveys a wrong impression. It is true that his widow had some difficulty in raising sufficient money to clear all her husband's business debts, and some were still outstanding when she died.[1] She was allowed two years to pay the legacies named in his will, and to produce the money required she was authorized to sell some of his real property, his 'partes and shares' in the Welsh mines, and, if necessary, four of his New River shares. Of these assets, it must be admitted, the real property, as the will shows, was mortgaged, the New River shares were of potential rather than immediate value, and for several years there was no bid for the mines. In spite of all this it would be misleading to describe the Myddeltons as poor. With a town house and a country house, well supplied with plate and jewellery, they had lived in style, and Sir Hugh's will certainly does not read like a poor man's will.[2]

He had already given his eldest surviving son, William, 'his full porcion which I intended to him out of my personall estate', therefore in his will he left him only £100, and £10 to his wife 'to buy her a ring'. His daughter Jane also had had her full portion, so she and her husband, Dr. Chamberlaine (or Chamberlen), were left £10 each to buy rings. His daughter Hester, who was to have £1,900 altogether, had already received £1,000, and the remaining £900 was to be held up until Lady Price (or Pryse), her husband's grandmother, had fulfilled certain obligations. Meanwhile Hester and her husband were each given £10 to buy rings. To his two other sons, Henry and Simon, he left £400 each; to his eldest daughter, Elizabeth, who was unmarried, £500.

[1] Cf. above, p. 83.
[2] It is printed in *Wills from Doctors' Commons* (Camden Soc., 1862 (1863)), pp. 92–98.

To his wife, who was to be sole executrix, with Robert Bateman and his nephews Thomas, Roger, and Richard Myddelton as 'overseers' of his will, Sir Hugh left 'all the chaines, rings, jewells, pearles, braceletts and gould buttons, which shee hath in her custodie, and useth to wear at festivalls. Also the deepe silver bason, the spout pot and maudlyn cupp of silver, and the smale bowle, all which were given her'. She was also to have a life interest in his shares in the New River Company, 'together with the rentes, arrerages of rentes, and proffites of them'. Lady Myddelton also had the house and land at Bush Hill, 'with all the household stuff and furniture therein, to have and to hould to her owne use ... during her naturall life', after which they were to pass to his youngest son Simon and his heirs. She was also to 'have the keeping and wearing of that great jewell which was given unto me by the Lord Maior of the cittie of London and aldermen of the same, and that she doe give and leave the same after her decease to such one of my sonnes as she shall thinke most worthy to weare and enjoye the same'.

Besides numerous small legacies to various named persons, including several nephews and their wives, and £5 each to all the men-servants 'who shalbe dwelling with me at the tyme of my decease' (except the kitchen boy, who got forty shillings, as did Elizabeth the maidservant), there were legacies of £20 to Robert Bateman, to buy a ring, and several employees of long standing were also recognized. Richard Newell was to receive £30, 'to the end he shall continue his care in the workes of the Mynes Royall wherein he is now ymployed'. Howell Jones, who likewise was to 'continue his care in the Water-Workes', received £20, as did Peter Hinde and his wife, 'to be devided betweene them', while the clerk of the New River Company, William Lewyn, was to have 'the yearly some of twenty poundes to be paid unto him every halfe yeare out of the rentes and proffittes of the said Waterworks, by equall porcions, for and duringe his naturall life, to the end that he shall doe his best endeavor for the advancement of the said Waterworkes'.

In addition to these legacies Sir Hugh left £20 'to the poore of the parish of Henllan, where I was borne', and the same 'to the poore of the towne of Denbigh'; 'to the poore of the parish of Amwell' he left £5. His principal charitable bequest, however, was a share in the New River Company, left to ten named 'citizens and gouldsmiths of London, and their successors, assistants of the Company of Gouldsmiths . . . for ever, upon trust' to distribute the profits arising from it, after his wife's death, 'in weekly porcions of twelve pence apeece to the poore of the said Company of Gouldsmiths . . . by the discretion of the wardens and assistants of the said company for the tyme beinge . . . , and especiallie to such poore men of my name, kindred or countrymen as are or shalbe free of the said companie'.

Besides the share thus left to the Goldsmiths' Company, five other New River shares were to be distributed, after Lady Myddelton's death, among his children, one each to his sons William, Henry, and Simon, and his daughters Elizabeth and Anne. He explains in his will that the undertaking is divided into two halves, one half being divided into thirty-six shares, thirteen of which 'are to myself belonging and are in the name of myself and other feoffees in trust to my use and the proffettes by me received', and the six shares bequeathed were to come out of these thirteen. The most probable explanation of this phraseology is that by the charter the company was to consist of twenty-nine Adventurers, and in order to make up this number Myddelton had had to convey some of his shares to nominees, who held them in trust for him.

In November 1633 Lady Myddelton sent to the Goldsmiths' Company a portrait of her late husband, with the request that it should be hung in their parlour, and the Court Minutes state that 'it shall be placed according to her desire'. This portrait, which is attributed to Cornelius Johnson (or Jansen) may be the one that still hangs in Goldsmiths' Hall.[1] The company also possesses a portrait by the same artist of Lady Myddelton, which now hangs alongside the portrait of Sir Hugh.[2] Lady Myddelton died on 19 July 1643, aged 63, and the bequest of a New River share to the Goldsmiths' Company should then have come into

[1] W. S. Prideaux, *Memorials of the Goldsmiths' Company*, i (1896), p. 159. See Appendix, p. 146.   [2] Purchased in 1897. See Appendix, pp. 147, 148.

effect, but Sir William Myddelton seems at first to have disputed the company's right to it until his father's debts had been paid off. This objection was overruled, however, and it was agreed that the company should appoint a representative as trustee 'to receive the profits of the company's share and to sit in Court with the Governor and Assistants of the New River Company'.[1]

Entries in the Court Minutes of the Goldsmiths' Company show that in administering Sir Hugh's charity the company did not exactly comply with the terms of his will, which had specified weekly doles of a shilling each. On 3 June 1646 the Court met 'to consider Sir Hugh Myddelton's will and the distribution of his gift', and a letter was read from Sir William Myddelton, recommending a kinsman and fellow-countryman of Sir Hugh's, Thomas Salisbury (?Salusbury). The clerk informed the Court that four half-yearly dividends had been received, amounting to £57. 12s. 1d.; £4. 17s. 4d. had been paid in expenses, and each half-year's dividend came to over £13, so that it would be possible to distribute £52 and still leave a small surplus. It was agreed that in future each half-yearly dividend should be disbursed as it came in, and that £52 should be distributed immediately among thirty-one recipients (including Thomas Salisbury) in sums varying from £1 to £5. 4s. A marginal note records that Robert Hooke refused the sum of £5. 4s. offered to him, and that it was therefore distributed among four other poor men.[2]

At a meeting of the Court at the beginning of the following July, when it was reported that the dividend for the half-year up to the preceding Lady Day amounted to £19. 8s. 8d., Lady Myddelton (Sir William's wife, that is) asked that 'some consideration' should be shown to the son of a widow named Howell, who was then at Cambridge. The wardens thought that this was contrary to the terms of Sir Hugh's will, but on Lady Myddelton 'pressing it so vehemently' they agreed to bring her request before the next Court of Assistants. The ultimate decision was that as Widow Howell's son, 'according to the testimony of Mr. Jackson the minister', was 'a hopeful religious young man', his mother should have twenty nobles for him, but she was to be told that this must not be regarded as a precedent.[1] The company seems to have found this Lady Myddelton rather difficult to deal with, for three months later the Court of Assistants was obliged to give orders for arrangements to be made for the dividends on their share to be paid direct to representatives of the company, 'because the last half year's dividend was paid to Lady Myddelton, which occasioned the Wardens to go to her in person for it, and with much difficulty they obtained payment thereof'.[2] The Goldsmiths' Company continued to hold their New River share until it was converted in 1904 into Metropolitan Water Board stock,[3] but Sir Hugh's bequest has now lost its separate identity, and the company's charities are mainly operated in a consolidated scheme.

Sir Hugh had fifteen children—seven sons and eight daughters —but a number of them, as often happened in those days, died in infancy; only three of his sons survived their father. Many writers have moralized over the decline of the family in succeeding generations. 'They certainly did not follow the example of their illustrious ancestor', we read. 'They took no active part in public affairs, and some of them it is to be feared were spendthrifts. The wealth with which their founder endowed them was soon lost, so that they gradually dwindled into obscurity and even to poverty, glad to accept of the bounty which the Corporation of the City of London, in recognition of the services of their great ancestor, generously placed at their disposal.'[4] This judgement is perhaps a little harsh, at any rate on the second baronet, who, if undistinguished, held a respectable position in the community; and we might remember that Sir Hugh's younger sons, the later offspring of a second marriage which took place when he was already in middle age, were young and inexperienced when their father died. With few exceptions, however, it is certainly true that in succeeding generations the decline of the family

---

[1] W. S. Prideaux, *Memorials of the Goldsmiths' Company*, i (1896), p. 244.

[2] Ibid., p. 245.

[3] Sir Hugh's charity was not always directly administered by the company, however. In 1694 the New River share was conveyed to Bartholomew Soames for ninety-nine years, in trust for the Warden and Assistants (ibid. ii (1897), p. 179). According to Stow's *Survey of London* (v. 60), a half-year's dividend in 1704 amounted to £134, and it was then customary to distribute the money among the poor in doles of 26s. each.

[4] W. Duncombe Pink, *Notes on the Middleton Family* (Chester, 1891), p. 32.

was hardly less than catastrophic, and, as one writer remarked, it 'afforded a melancholy proof of a fact, the truth of which we have too frequent evidence of, namely, that a man may convey his blood, but not his brains, to his posterity'.[1]

Sir William Myddelton, the second baronet and his father's third son, was born in 1603. Besides succeeding Sir Hugh as Governor of the New River Company, he became Governor of Denbigh Castle (a position previously held, in succession to his grandfather, by his uncle Charles Myddelton), assessment commissioner for the county, and a burgess or councillor for the borough of Denbigh. In the Civil War he took up arms on the Roundhead side, and attained the rank of colonel. A warrant he received from the Earl of Essex early in January 1644 gives us a glimpse of the difficulties commanders had to contend with, especially when their men's pay was in arrears. Sir William was 'to make search in and about London and Westminster' for all sorts of army property ('horses, mares, geldings and nags', as well as 'arms, pikes, muskets' and other equipment) which had been stolen, sold, or pawned. Later in the same year he brought reinforcements from London to his Chirk Castle cousin, Sir Thomas Myddelton II, 'Major-General for North Wales', at a critical time when the royalists were gathering to besiege Oswestry. Although in the summer the joint Myddelton forces were said to be 'much diminished for want of pay', by the autumn Sir Thomas was able to report a series of victories—Oswestry relieved, and Montgomery Castle and other places captured.[2] Sir William Myddelton married Eleanor, daughter of Sir Thomas Harris, of Shrewsbury, baronet; he died in 1652.

The fifth son, Henry, who was born in 1607, seems to have had an honourable if not particularly remarkable career. In May 1628 he was a student at Gray's Inn; shortly before his father's death he was sworn a burgess of Denbigh. In December 1637 he was appointed Keeper of His Majesty's Garden, distiller of 'sweete herbes and waters', and Keeper of the Library at Whitehall.

[1] *Gentleman's Magazine*, liv (1784), p. 805. The following summary account of Sir Hugh's descendants is based chiefly on the pedigree by G. Milner-Gibson-Cullum in *Miscellanea Genealogica et Heraldica*, 3rd series, vol. ii, part 8 (Dec. 1897), pp. 270 ff.

[2] *Cal. S.P.D. 1644*, pp. 1–2, 65, 194, 284, 533; *1644–5*, p. 3.

When the Civil War broke out he took the parliamentary side, like his brother William, and was in command of a troop of horse under the Earl of Manchester. At the end of the war he was Sergeant of Mace attending the Great Seal, and he was one of those appointed to attend on the King at Holmby House in 1647. Rather more is known (and little of it to his credit) about Simon, the seventh and youngest son, born about 1612, who inherited the house at Bush Hill after his mother's death, and seems to have been something of a favourite. At first he was apprenticed to a Merchant-Taylor; in 1651 he was carrying on business as a Woollen Draper in a house on the south side of St. Paul's church-yard, but he does not seem to have pursued this or any other career for long. On 21 March 1641 he had been granted the freedom of the Goldsmiths' Company by patrimony,[1] and in 1653 he was admitted a member of Gray's Inn. In 1658 he acquired the King's Moiety of the New River from his nephew, the third baronet,[2] and, possibly about the same time, became Treasurer of the New River Company. How long he held this office is uncer-tain, but he seems to have misconducted himself, and the company had to get rid of him. A few years later, however, he applied for the post of clerk, and produced a letter of recommendation from Charles II, stating that as he held the King's Moiety in fee farm, this would be a pledge for his integrity.[3] The company, however, was not at all anxious to employ him again, and when his applica-tion was discussed at a Court meeting one member 'spoke slightingly' of his letter from the King, 'said that such were to be had for 5s. each', and 'declared during the reading that it was false, and would hardly let it be read through'.[4] The court refused to accept him, stating that 'he was once mad, and spoke traitorous speeches, and would be apt to relapse'. Moreover, while Treasurer he had 'detained the profits of divers shares, and when dismissed refused to give up the key of the chest'. He had 'put the company to much cost' in lawsuits, and was unfit for the responsibilities

[1] W. S. Prideaux, *Memorials of the Goldsmiths' Company*, i (1896), p. 197.
[2] Cf. below, p. 138.
[3] *Cal. S.P.D. 1664–5*, p. 303 (11 Apr. 1665).
[4] Ibid., p. 324.

of clerk, a post which in any case was 'beneath his estate and dignity'.[1]

Simon attempted to justify himself in reply to these charges. The 'traitorous words' he was reported to have uttered 'were said in a violent fever, in which his mind was distempered'; the suits brought against him by Sir William Backhouse and others were 'unjust'; the company paid 'extravagant allowances . . . to Sir William's serving man', which he would reduce if he became clerk, and so on.[2] By this time the King's Moiety was bringing in a substantial income—£2,000 a year was the figure he mentioned—but he may in time have come to regret his connexion with the New River, for the lawsuits in which he was involved dragged on for years, and ultimately were decided against him.[3] After this we lose sight of him, except that in 1673 he presented a portrait of his father to the Goldsmiths' Company.[4] He was four times married, and maintained some position in society, for his daughter Sarah married Robert Harley, Earl of Oxford, and on 6 December 1681 his son Hugh was created a baronet in his own right, as Sir Hugh Myddelton of Hackney. The latter seems to have been unbalanced like his father, and quite unworthy of the title. His marriage to Dorothy Oglander broke down[5] and he squandered his estate. In the early eighteenth century he was living in poverty at Kemberton in Shropshire, where he was said at one time to be employed as a labourer paving the street, under the name of William Raymond. He was buried at Shifnal on 11 March 1702.[6] This baronetcy, which then became extinct, was quite distinct from the first Sir Hugh's baronetcy of Ruthin, but the existence of two Sir Hugh Myddeltons in the later seventeenth century sometimes caused them to be confused.[7]

Sir Hugh Myddelton, the third baronet, was Sir William's eldest son. Unlike his father, he favoured the royalist cause, and during the Interregnum he was twice imprisoned (in 1652 and 1659), for plotting on behalf of Charles II. On the first occasion

[1] Ibid., p. 315.   [2] Ibid., p. 324.   [3] Cf. below, p. 138.
[4] W. S. Prideaux, *Memorials of the Goldsmiths' Company*, ii (1897), p. 168. See Appendix, p. 146.   [5] Cf. above, p. 97.
[6] *Gentleman's Magazine*, lxxix (1809), p. 795.
[7] Cf. the note by J. L. Chester in *Westminster Abbey Register* (Harleian Soc. vol. x, 1876), p. 21, on which later accounts of the family history are based.

he was bought out by his relatives at Chirk Castle; after the Restoration he became gentleman-usher to the Duke of York.[1] Realizing that his son could not be trusted with property, Sir William had taken the precaution, in 1646, of conveying the King's Moiety, which he held, to his brother Henry and three other trustees, first of all on behalf of Sir William himself and his wife, during their lives, and subsequently, after certain provisions for his daughters, to pay the income to his son Hugh. The needy Hugh, however, seems to have persuaded his uncle Henry to allow him control of the capital, and in June 1657 he made a contract to sell fourteen shares to a certain William Bishop for £7,000.[2] In the following December, and before this transaction had been completed, there came a more tempting offer from his uncle Simon. He closed with this, and in January 1658 he and Henry executed a conveyance of the whole King's Moiety to Simon for £15,100. Bishop immediately challenged this sale and brought an action to enforce the execution of the previous contract for the sale of fourteen shares to him. This was the beginning of a long series of legal proceedings in Chancery, in the course of which the death of Bishop and two subsequent re-marriages of his widow[3] introduced a number of technical legal points that were argued at length.[4] The case dragged on until 1671, when it was finally decided that Lady Cornbury, as she then was, should get her fourteen shares, and further that, in accordance with a clause in the original contract with Bishop, these shares should be exempt from contributing towards the Crown Clog, which therefore was to be charged on the remaining twenty-two shares.[5]

[1] He had a younger brother, John, who was killed, unmarried, on board Sir Edward Spragge's ship in the sea-fight in Sole Bay on 3 June 1665. One of his three sisters, Elizabeth, married John Grene, or Greene, the clerk to the New River Company.

[2] This is the first mention of a sale of shares in the King's Moiety. In 1663 he hopefully, but unsuccessfully, petitioned for a grant of the reversion of the Crown Clog (cf. above, p. 82).

[3] Her second husband was Sir William Backhouse, whose family had been connected with the New River from the earliest days. Her third husband was Lord Cornbury.

[4] Other difficulties arose from doubts whether Sir Hugh, being only *cestui que trust* and not absolute owner of the King's Moiety, could make valid contracts to sell the shares at all, whether to Bishop or to his uncle Simon.

[5] The case is reported in *Cases argued and decreed in the High Court of Chancery* (2nd

The third baronet married three times, and it has been said that he had no issue, and that the baronetcy became extinct at his death, in the winter of 1675–6. In fact, however, by his third wife he had a son Hugh, who succeeded as fourth baronet. He was sworn a burgess of Denbigh in 1681, and, like his father, seems to have been a hanger-on about the Court: in 1685 he was a Gentleman of the Privy Chamber. He also became a member of the Goldsmiths' Company, and on 30 June 1682 was elected Upper Warden.[1] His wedding to a lady of property took place in Westminster Abbey, and with him the decline in the family's position seems for the moment to have been arrested, if not actually reversed. His son Sir Hugh Myddelton, the fifth baronet, became a captain in the Royal Navy, later retiring to Chigwell, in Essex, but with his son, Sir Hugh Myddelton, the sixth baronet, the fortunes of the family collapsed utterly. His widowed mother was reduced to dependence on the charity of the Goldsmiths' Company, who paid her a pension of £20.[2] 'At the solicitation of Mr. Harvey, of Chigwell', according to one correspondent, 'this pension was continued to her son Sir Hugh', though he also had some other property and it was not his only means of support. His sole employment and amusement, we read, 'consisted in drinking ale in any company he could pick up. Mr. Harvey took care of him, and put him to board in the house of a sober farmer at or near Chigwell, on whom he could depend.'[3] A correspondent who was at school at Chigwell remembered this Sir Hugh as 'a tall, thin man, very profligate and addicted to all manner of low vices'. He had such a bad reputation that 'the report of his being in the village . . . so frightened us children that we always

---

edn. 1707), pp. 173 ff., 208 ff. Besides the Clog of £500 a year there was an annuity of £100 to Henry Myddelton for life, presumably arranged by Sir William when he appointed Henry as a trustee. Simon thus found himself with a diminished investment but undiminished liabilities. If in order to meet them he, or possibly his son, later found it necessary to raise more money, this may perhaps be part of the explanation of the odd arrangement by which the Crown Clog fell on one or two Adventurers' shares as well as some of the King's shares. Cf. above, p. 82.

[1] Presumably equivalent to Prime Warden, which he was also called (W. S. Prideaux, *Memorials of the Goldsmiths' Company*, ii (1897), pp. 172, 173).

[2] She also apparently had a government pension of £60, but in 1752 was in distress through non-payment of it (*N. & Q.*, 3rd series, ii (1862), p. 410).

[3] *Gentleman's Magazine*, liv (1784), p. 805.

locked ourselves up in our rooms'. He died in or about 1757, 'unmarried, in extreme poverty . . . , in a barn belonging to Mr. Brown, who then kept the White Hart', and was buried at the expense of the parish.[1]

This unfortunate man was the last to bear the title, but it was not yet legally extinct. The first Sir Hugh's fifth son, Henry, had a son of the same name who became a surgeon and attended Robert Harley, Earl of Oxford.[2] He left two sons, the elder of whom, Starkey Myddelton, also a surgeon, died and was buried in Bath Abbey in 1755.[3] The younger, Henry, had a son, also called Starkey, who after beginning life as a bell-founder subsequently became a Methodist minister. He lived at West Ham, and died, apparently in reduced circumstances, in 1768. This Starkey Myddelton had two sons, the elder of whom, Joseph, died in 1787; the younger, Jabez, lived at Hoxton and had a pension of a pound a week from the Corporation of London in consideration of his descent. It would presumably have been open to him, or to his father and elder brother, to have claimed the baronetcy which had become dormant on the death of the sixth baronet, but the likelihood is that they preferred not to assume an empty title when they could not live up to it. They undoubtedly were aware of their lineage, and Joseph kept a journal (now in the possession of Dr. G. C. Myddelton, of Parkside, Henley-on-Thames), in which he entered particulars of various members of his family and their marriages, with a drawing of Sir Hugh's coat of arms and his motto, *Virtus Palma*. With the death of Jabez Myddelton, on 27 March 1828, the line of direct male descent from the first Sir Hugh came to an end. He left three daughters, of whom the third on her father's death petitioned the Corporation of London for a pension, stating that her father had been 'the last male representative of Sir Hugh Middleton'.[4] She died a widow, aged 78, on 23 March 1863, and was buried in Bow Cemetery.

[1] *Gentleman's Magazine*, lxii (1792), p. 720.

[2] Harley married Simon Myddelton's daughter Sarah as his second wife.

[3] One of his sons was also a surgeon; another, styled 'gentleman', died in the West Indies.

[4] One of her father's sisters had been granted a pension by the Corporation of London in 1794; it was increased to £50 in Dec. 1801.

The extinction of the baronetcy, however, does not mean that the whole family has died out. Numerous descendants of Sir Hugh are alive today, and some, at any rate, have fared better than the male line. Such for example was the Devonshire family of Ellacombe (or Ellicombe, as the name was formerly spelt), descendants of the Rev. Richard Ellicombe, of Stoke Canon, near Exeter, who married Miss Greene, Sir Hugh Myddelton's great-granddaughter.[1] She was the owner of four Adventurers' shares, two of which remained continuously in the family's possession until the end of the New River as a separate concern. The last holder, Canon H. N. Ellacombe, vicar of Bitton, near Bristol, took a keen interest in the affairs of the New River Company until it was absorbed by the Metropolitan Water Board; he then became a member of the board of the New River Co. Ltd., and attended meetings regularly till shortly before his death, at the age of ninety-six, in 1916. It is interesting to note that the canon's father, like one of his uncles, General Charles Ellicombe, seems to have inherited some of his great ancestor's engineering talents and interests. He devoted all his leisure, we read, to mechanical drawing and the construction of models, and was engaged for a time as assistant to Sir Marc Brunel,[2] but later gave up an engineering career and took holy orders.[3]

More often, however, Sir Hugh's nineteenth-century descendants seem to have been people in humble if not actually indigent circumstances. After Jabez Myddelton's death in 1828 the Corporation of London felt obliged to pass a resolution to the effect that they would grant no more relief to members of the family,[4]

[1] Her father John Grene, or Greene, married Elizabeth, a daughter of Sir William Myddelton, the second baronet (cf. p. 138, n. 1, above).

[2] Isambard Kingdom Brunel's father.

[3] Cf. A. W. Hill (ed.), *Henry Nicholson Ellacombe . . . a Memoir* (1919). Both H. N. Ellacombe and his father (H. T. Ellacombe) were at Oriel College, Oxford. H. N. Ellacombe's garden at Bitton vicarage became celebrated, and he transmitted his interest in horticulture to E. A. Bowles, of Myddelton House, near Enfield, whose father he used to meet on the New River Company's board. On Bowles's house and garden, which borders on the old course of the New River, see W. T. Stearn's obituary article in *Journal R. Horticultural Soc.* lxxx, part 7 (1955), p. 317, though the story about the diversion of the river appears to be unfounded. It follows the lie of the land.

[4] Cf. S. Lewis, *History and Topography of the Parish of St. Mary, Islington* (1842), p. 430.

but somehow the idea grew up that the New River Company held a large sum which was only waiting to be claimed by Sir Hugh's descendants. It seems to have been believed that when the company was founded Sir Hugh had parted with his entire interest in return for an annuity of £100[1] to himself and his heirs for ever, that this had not been claimed since about 1715, and that consequently the company held a large accumulation of arrears which could be recovered by a properly authenticated claimant. On 29 May 1837, we read, an advertisement actually appeared in *Bell's Weekly Messenger*, calling upon Sir Hugh's descendants to claim the sum of £10,000, then lying in the Bank of England, and in 1843 the Lord Mayor of London is said to have written to the Mayor of Denbigh, inquiring whether any known descendants of Sir Hugh were to be found there.[2]

Of course no such sum existed, nor did the Goldsmiths' Company hold anything of Sir Hugh's except the one share he had bequeathed for charity. But wild rumours were in circulation in and around Denbigh, and hopes based on them were apparently encouraged by a man named M. L. Louis, author of a little book called *Gleanings in North Wales*. There is a rather pathetic story of how he and one of the claimants travelled up to London for an interview with the chairman of the New River Company's directors, after which they paid an equally futile visit to Goldsmiths' Hall.[3] These vain hopes were due to ignorance, and in any case residents at Denbigh more probably belonged to other branches of the Myddelton family rather than to Sir Hugh's. Nevertheless an indirect result of these distresses was to stimulate a public interest in Sir Hugh and his family which had already been manifested in the later years of the eighteenth century in a series of contributions to the *Gentleman's Magazine*.[4] Genea-

---

[1] This misapprehension may have arisen from confusion with an annuity at one time payable to Sir Hugh's son Henry: cf. above, p. 138, n. 5.

[2] *Archaeologia Cambrensis*, 2nd series, no. 1 (1850), pp. 137, 138 n.; J. Williams, *Ancient and Modern Denbigh* (Denbigh, 1856), p. 157 n.

[3] J. Williams, op. cit., p. 160. The author says that Lord Campbell had told him that he had been 'several times applied to' on behalf of Sir Hugh's descendants, but had no power to interfere (ibid., p. 162).

[4] In vols. liv (1784) and lxii (1792). The latter volume contains a number of contributions from and discussions between several correspondents.

logists established facts about his family, articles were written about him,[1] he figured in Edmund Lodge's *Portraits of Illustrious Personages of Great Britain*,[2] and his work was summarized in local histories. In mid-Victorian times his name had become widely known as a public benefactor, his will was selected for publication by the Camden Society, and he was given a place in the *Dictionary of National Biography*.

His fame was also commemorated by the erection of visible memorials. The first of these, set up in 1800, was Robert Mylne's urn on the island in the New River at Amwell;[3] in 1845 a statue of Sir Hugh by Samuel Joseph was placed in a niche on the north side of the newly rebuilt Royal Exchange. Then in 1862 a marble statue, in Elizabethan costume, by the sculptor John Thomas, together with a drinking-fountain (the joint gift of Sir Samuel Morton Peto, the New River Company, and subscribers among the local inhabitants) was erected on Islington Green. It was inaugurated by Mr. Gladstone, then Chancellor of the Exchequer. He 'drank from a silver cup some of the water, pledging therein the healths of the company', who then 'adjourned to the new Agricultural Hall', where Mr. Gladstone 'in a lengthy speech referred to the benefits which had been conferred on society by the great work of Sir Hugh Myddelton, and eulogised his indomitable energy and perseverance'.[4]

These are the qualities that every biographer of Sir Hugh cannot help stressing. He had no mathematical or other technical training, as far as we know, as a civil engineer, and relied on professional assistants. But apart from his success in overcoming obstacles, his energy was manifested in the variety of tasks that he undertook at the same time. When we consider the difficulties of travel in the seventeenth century, it is astonishing that one man was able, simultaneously, to direct mining operations in

[1] A quite well-informed specimen, one of a series on 'The Merchant Princes of England', appeared in *London Society*, vol. vi (1864), pp. 455–66. The first edition of Samuel Smiles's *Lives of the Engineers* had appeared in 1861.

[2] Vol. 5 (1826).

[3] Cf. above, p. 85.

[4] W. J. Pinks, *History of Clerkenwell* (1865), pp. 466, 467. There used to be another statue of Sir Hugh, by Henry Bursill, at Holborn Viaduct, but it was destroyed by enemy action during the Second World War.

remote Cardiganshire, reclaim land in the Isle of Wight, and also carry the chief responsibility for the New River in its early unprofitable years. Yet in about 1621 he was doing all this, in addition to his other activities as a goldsmith and a Member of Parliament. 'I cannot be idle', he once told Sir John Salusbury,[1] and he spoke the truth. When Sir John Wynn invited him to reclaim Traeth Mawr, he wrote of his 'love to publique works', and one feels his regret at having to decline. He was an elderly man by then, and even he had to admit that he could add no more to his burden. He had received honours from the King, and universal acclaim for his work, but he never boasted of it. 'Few are the things done by me', he wrote, 'for which I give God the glory'.[2] The grammar is imperfect, but we cannot mistake what he meant.

[1] Cf. above, p. 12.
[2] Cf. above, p. 98. The old motto of the Goldsmiths' Company (and of the Skinners) was 'To God only be all Glory'.

APPENDIX

PORTRAITS OF SIR HUGH MYDDELTON

ALTHOUGH apparently no signature has been detected on it, Sir Hugh Myddelton's portrait is generally attributed to Cornelius Johnson (sometimes spelt Jansen or Janssen, and sometimes also called Johnson van Ceulen), a fashionable painter of portraits of the English nobility and gentry in the early seventeenth century. He is depicted wearing the jewel and chain given him by the Corporation of London on the completion of the New River, with one hand resting on a shell, from which water pours, and with the words *Fontes Fodinae* just above it. At the top of the picture on the right are his arms, and on the left the inscription *Aetatis sue 68 Anno Do 1628*. A number of versions of this portrait are in existence, either undated or later in date than this, and I think we may presume that they are replicas or copies. Several are associated with, and may have been commissioned by, Sir Hugh's youngest son Simon. One, and perhaps two, of these replicas were painted by Johnson himself; of the rest, some certainly and others probably are later copies.

What appears to be the original, for which Sir Hugh sat (or stood) in 1628, must have passed to his daughter Jane, who married Dr. Peter Chamberlen, of Woodham Mortimer, near Maldon, in Essex, the inventor of the obstetric forceps.[1] By the latter part of the eighteenth century this portrait was in the possession of John Luther, of Great Myles's, near Chipping Ongar,[2] whose father Richard had married Dr. Chamberlen's granddaughter Charlotte. John Luther died without issue in 1786, and the portrait then passed, with his estate, to Francis Fane, the younger son of John Luther's sister Charlotte, who had married Henry Fane, of Wormsley, near Stokenchurch, Bucks.[3] It remained with the Fane family at Wormsley until 1885, when it was sold at Christie's for £514. 10s.,[4] and bought by a dealer named Noseda on

[1] J. H. Aveling, *The Chamberlens and the Midwifery Forceps* (1882), p. 122. Jane and her husband are mentioned in Sir Hugh's will (above, p. 130).

[2] J. Granger, *Biographical History of England, Supplement* (1774), p. 140.

[3] *V.C.H. Essex*, iv. 68. Stokenchurch was then in Oxfordshire; it was transferred to Bucks in 1896. See *V.C.H. Bucks*. iii. 34, 99.

[4] A large sum for that time, which supports the inference that this was the original portrait. Later copies have fetched only £50 or £60 at sales.

L

behalf of a Mrs. Frick (later Mrs. Frick Jacobs). She bequeathed it to the Museum of Art at Baltimore, Maryland, where it now is.

Another version of the same portrait is in the Duke of Portland's collection at Welbeck Abbey. This appears to have come into the possession of Robert Harley, Earl of Oxford, through his wife Sarah, Simon Myddelton's daughter, and was inherited by the Duchess of Portland in 1742, when Harley's collection was dispersed after the death of the second earl.[1] It was engraved by George Vertue in 1722, with a note 'C.J. fe[cit]. 1632' beneath the bottom right-hand corner; and a statement in Vertue's notebook[2] seems to imply that this date was on the picture itself. It is usually said that there is now no date on the picture, but Mr. David Piper, of the National Portrait Gallery, tells me that Mr. Oliver Millar can vouch for the existence of both date and signature, though they are small and elusive. This must have been a posthumous replica of the original portrait, and I gather that there are plenty of parallels for Johnson repeating his own compositions.

Another version, also claimed as Johnson's work, hangs in the Court Room at Goldsmiths' Hall. This has the date 1631 on the frame, and may be the portrait presented by Lady Myddelton in November 1633.[3] In April 1673, however, the company received another portrait of Sir Hugh from his son Simon;[4] yet there is now only one portrait at Goldsmiths' Hall, and nothing seems to be known about a second. A conceivable explanation, though it is only a conjecture, is that the picture given by Lady Myddelton may have perished in the Great Fire of 1666, and that Simon's gift was made as a replacement. According to the Goldsmiths' records it was 'donne at the charge of the said Mr. Middleton, and by him given to this Company, for that the Court of Assistants did excuse him from the small service of the 3rd. and 2nd. Warden's places without paying anything for the same'. On the bottom of the frame was the inscription: IN GRATAM MEMORIAM VIRI PRAECLARISSIMI HUGONIS MIDDLETON, BARRONETT, HUJUS SOCIETATIS MEMBRI ET BENEFACTORIS DIGNISSIMI, ANNO DOMINI 1644.[5] There is

---

[1] See R. W. Goulding and C. K. Adams, *Catalogue of the Pictures belonging to . . . the Duke of Portland* (Cambridge, 1936), p. 38.

[2] B.M. Add. MS. 23068, f. 81: 'Cornelius Johnson painted the picture of Sir Rob. Cotton Anº 1629 so consequently he was then in England and as may be seen . . . by the Picture of Sir Hugh Middleton belonging to the Earl of Oxford dated 1632 he was still heare. . . .'

[3] Above, p. 132. Aubrey mentions the portrait in Goldsmiths' Hall, and says Myddelton had 'a Waterpott by him'.

[4] Above, p. 137.

[5] W. S. Prideaux, *Memorials of the Goldsmiths' Company*, ii. 168.

no such inscription or date on the present frame, but in any case this is of a later date, probably about 1725 or after. The date 1644 may have referred to the coming into effect of Sir Hugh's benefaction to the company after Lady Myddelton's death.

Her portrait also hangs in the Court Room at Goldsmiths' Hall, and the frame bears the date 1643, but (unless it is a copy) it must have been painted long before that, for it shows her dressed in a costume of about 1610–15, when she would have been in her early thirties, and this tallies with her appearance. This portrait, which was formerly at Belchamp Hall, in Essex, was bought by the Goldsmiths' Company in 1897. The date 1643 was the year of her death, and the date 1631 now on the frame of Sir Hugh's portrait may also refer to his death rather than to the year when it was painted.

In 1857 the Goldsmiths' Company were asked to lend their portrait of Sir Hugh Myddelton for an exhibition at Manchester, but they declined to do so, and the version from Welbeck was exhibited instead. A notice of the exhibition in *The Times* (13 April 1857), saying 'There is a copy in Goldsmiths' Hall, but the picture in the exhibition is the original', elicited an indignant letter to *The Athenaeum*,[1] declaring that the Goldsmiths' portrait (mentioned in the official catalogue of the exhibition as a 'duplicate' of the one at Welbeck) had been 'pronounced by competent judges an original', and was 'the recognized portrait of Sir Hugh Myddelton', so that the Welbeck portrait must have been the copy. In fact both are presumably copies, or replicas. If the Goldsmiths' portrait is the one presented by Lady Myddelton in 1633 it may, like the Welbeck version, have been painted by Johnson himself; but if it is Simon's gift, the likelihood is that it is a later copy, made from one of the other versions. The catalogue of the Duke of Portland's pictures, which gives some particulars of various versions, describes the Goldsmiths' portrait as presented by Simon. It was this version that was engraved by E. Scriven for Edmund Lodge's *Portraits of Illustrious Persons of Great Britain*.[2]

A pair of portraits, of Sir Hugh and Lady Myddelton, both ascribed to 'Cornelius Jansen', were shown at an exhibition at South Kensington in 1866, when they belonged to the Rev. J. M. St. Clere Raymond.[3] He lived at Belchamp Walter, in Essex, where, as a tablet in the church shows, his ancestors had lived since the early seventeenth century. Both portraits are mentioned as being at Belchamp Hall, then the

[1] No. 1542 (16 May 1857), p. 634. [2] Vol. v (1826).
[3] See *Catalogue of the Special Exhibition of National Portraits* (1866), pp. 81, 82.

residence of the Rev. Samuel Raymond, in 1803.[1] Like the portraits at Welbeck and at Goldsmiths' Hall, this pair can also be traced back to Simon Myddelton, who acquired Goldingham Hall from the Soame family by his marriage to his second wife, Mary Soame. Goldingham Hall is in Bulmer parish, but it is less than a mile from Belchamp Hall, across a small stream. It became the residence of Simon's son Hugh (Sir Hugh Myddelton of Hackney),[2] who died in penury under the name of Raymond:[3] whether he had any connexion with the Raymond family other than having been their neighbour in Essex is unknown, but his use of their name can hardly have been a coincidence, and the Raymonds presumably acquired the portraits from him or from his estate. After Mr. St. Clere Raymond's death in 1894 these portraits were sold. The portrait of Lady Myddelton was bought by the Goldsmiths' Company as a companion to the portrait they already possessed of her husband. Sir Hugh's portrait came into the possession of T. H. Ismay, the founder of the White Star Line. His collection of pictures was sold at Christie's on 4 April 1908, and this portrait was described in the catalogue of the sale as being by 'C. Janssen', but the price paid for it (fifty guineas) suggests that it was a copy. Since then it has had more than one owner, and it now belongs to Mr. and Mrs. Richard S. Frankel, of Woodside, California.

Yet another version, also attributed to Cornelius Johnson, used to belong to the New River Company. It was lost in the fire at their office in 1769, and in 1773 they paid Nathaniel Hone £42 to paint a copy of the Goldsmiths' portrait. This now hangs in one of the committee rooms at the Metropolitan Water Board's offices. There is also a copy of the Johnson portrait at the National Portrait Gallery. This was bought at Christie's in 1928 for £60 from Major G. F. M. Cornwallis-West of Ruthin, and according to a statement (dated 16 January 1929) by Mr. R. F. Myddelton, of Colne Mead, Rickmansworth, it was formerly at Gwaenynog, in the possession of his grandfather, the Rev. Robert Myddelton, who sold it in the 1870's to a dealer in Chester,[4] from whom it was bought by Major Cornwallis-West's father. Col. R. Myddelton has another copy of the Johnson portrait at Chirk Castle, possibly the one which, according to a note at the National Portrait

[1] E. W. Brayley and J. Britton, *The Beauties of England and Wales*, v. 371–2.

[2] Cf. P. Morant, *History and Antiquities of the County of Essex* (1768), ii. 310, but the account confuses Simon with his father.

[3] Above, p. 137.

[4] According to W. M. Myddelton, *Pedigree of the Family of Myddelton*, p. 1, the Rev. Robert Myddelton sold Gwaenynog in 1870.

Gallery, was bought at a sale in London in 1859. Where it came from seems to be unknown.

There is also quite a different portrait at Chirk Castle, ascribed in the catalogue to Anthonisz van Ravesteyn, but this is so unlike the Johnson portrait that I doubt if it can be a portrait of Sir Hugh. Yet another, and again very different portrait, is now at the Science Museum, South Kensington,[1] to which it came in 1903 through the bequest of the widow of Bennet Woodcroft, F.R.S. (1803–77), Professor of Machinery at University College, London. Mr. A. Stowers, Deputy Keeper of the Science Museum, has kindly examined this portrait and tells me that it has a piece of paper stuck on the back with the one word 'Myddleton'. It was said to be a portrait of Sir Hugh, but it represents an elderly man in the costume of about 1600, and in any case is quite unlike him. It may conceivably be a portrait of some other member of the Myddelton family. Mr. Berry tells me he has a photograph of a portrait, supposed to be of Sir Hugh (but not like him), which belonged to Francis Morgan, of Romsey, Hants, who obtained it at the death, in 1878, of the Rt. Hon. Sir Thomas Myddelton-Biddulph, K.C.B., of Chirk Castle. This also may represent some other member of the family.

The inn-sign in Hogarth's *Evening* (the third of his 'Four Times of Day' series) bears the representation of a head with the name of Sir Hugh Myddelton beneath it. This is interesting as evidence of Sir Hugh's fame in the eighteenth century, but it is not a likeness.

[1] It is reproduced in W. H. G. Armytage, *A Social History of Engineering* (1961), facing p. 65.

INDEX

PRINTED IN GREAT BRITAIN
AT THE UNIVERSITY PRESS, OXFORD
BY VIVIAN RIDLER
PRINTER TO THE UNIVERSITY